About this publication

This history of jet fighters combines the talents of David Anderton, a writer whose involvement with the subject has been long and intense, and John Batchelor, who turns his unique ability as an illustrator to this fascinating subject.

We cover the development of the jet fighter from the early days of Heinkel and Whittle, through the Second World War and all the wars since then, up to the present day and beyond. The author, a technical consultant who specialises in forecasting trends in technical developments, includes his ideas on the future of jet fighters, and rounds off the story with a chapter on fighter armament.

The dazzling full colour illustrations by John Batchelor combine with a lavish use of photographs to show virtually every important jet fighter of the past 35 years, right up to the YF-16 and its contemporaries that will be the fighters of the future.

W9-CIR-530

Northrop F-89 Scorpion all-weather interceptor

Flight International

David Anderton's professional and technical qualifications are too numerous to list in detail. He graduated in Aeronautical engineering in 1941, and during the Second World War worked for Grumman on, among other projects, the F8F-1 Bearcat and F9F-1 Panther, before being appointed Consultant to Grumman on unconventional powerplants. Later, with General Electric, he was Project Engineer for the Hermes B missile programme. In 1950 he joined McGraw Hill as an Associate Editor of *Aviation Week*, eventually becoming Technical Editor of the magazine. Since 1963 he has run his own technical consultancy on aerospace, his forte being the forecasting of trends in technical developments.

John Batchelor, after serving in the RAF, worked in the technical publications departments of several British aircraft firms, and went on to contribute on a freelance basis to many technical magazines. Since then, his work for Purnell's Histories of the World Wars, and subsequently the Purnell's World War Specials, has established him as one of the most outstanding artists in his field. A total enthusiast, he takes every opportunity to fly, sail, drive or shoot with any piece of military equipment he can find.

JET FIGHTERS

By David A Anderton
and John Batchelor

Editor   Bernard Fitzsimons
Designers   Graham Ambrose
                          Stuart Cowley
Picture Research   Anne Williams
Production Editor   Frank Sloan

Published by Marshall Cavendish Promotions Ltd 1975
Printed in USA
© 1975 Phoebus Publishing Company/BPC Publishing Ltd

RAF McDonnell Phantom intercepts a Russian Bear

MOD

This narrative follows the common threads of a single subject: the jet fighter. Here a fighter is defined as an aircraft designed to destroy other aircraft as a primary mission. This rules out those planes which were designed primarily for strike or ground attack, even though they may have remaining capability as fighters to claw their way back from the target area.

The chapters that deal with the development of the jet fighter are divided to follow that development in one country at a time. Further, the arrangement is chronological, with the key time being the date of the first flight of either a fighter prototype or of the research aircraft that immediately preceded development of a jet fighter:

Two types of basic jet propulsion powerplants are considered here. One is the rocket engine, a self-contained motor burning a liquid fuel and oxidiser, and generating its thrust by combustion of the two in a suitably shaped chamber and exhaust nozzle. The other is the aircraft gas turbine for jet propulsion, an engine which takes in outside air, mixes it with fuel, burns the mixture, and exhausts the hot gases at high speed through a suitable nozzle.

Neither engine type was new when it was first applied to aircraft. The rocket engine, albeit in the form of a solid-propellant system, had been known for years, and was familiar to millions in the form of fireworks. They had been used in warfare and, in the daring years of flight during the 1920s, they had been adapted to launch a glider into the air in the first recorded flight of any aircraft anywhere using jet propulsion of any type.

But that experiment, demonstrated by the Opel-Sander Rakete 1 on 30 September 1929 at Frankfurt, led to a dead end. Neither the state of the solid-propellant rocket art nor that of aeroplane design was ready then for the use of such a novel form of propulsion.

The gas turbine is also an old form of powerplant. The first patent for such an engine

"THIS IS HEINKEL. WE'VE JUST FLOWN THE WORLD'S FIRST JET FIGHTER!"

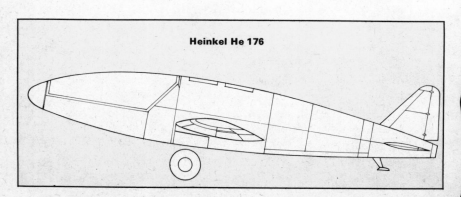

Heinkel He 176

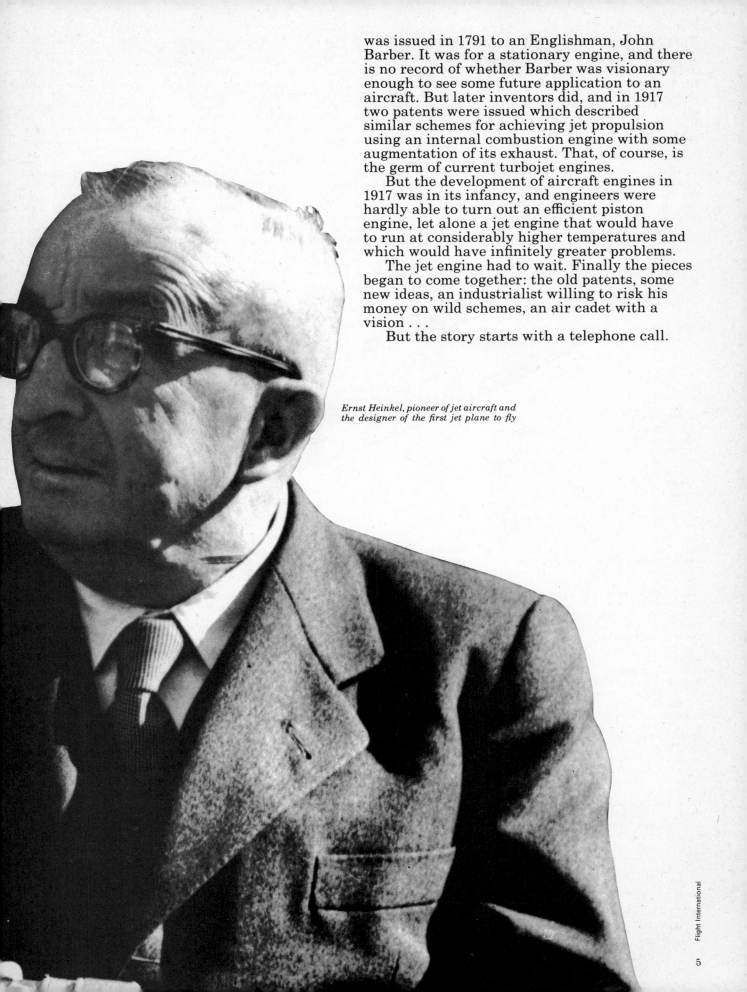

was issued in 1791 to an Englishman, John Barber. It was for a stationary engine, and there is no record of whether Barber was visionary enough to see some future application to an aircraft. But later inventors did, and in 1917 two patents were issued which described similar schemes for achieving jet propulsion using an internal combustion engine with some augmentation of its exhaust. That, of course, is the germ of current turbojet engines.

But the development of aircraft engines in 1917 was in its infancy, and engineers were hardly able to turn out an efficient piston engine, let alone a jet engine that would have to run at considerably higher temperatures and which would have infinitely greater problems.

The jet engine had to wait. Finally the pieces began to come together: the old patents, some new ideas, an industrialist willing to risk his money on wild schemes, an air cadet with a vision . . .

But the story starts with a telephone call.

Ernst Heinkel, pioneer of jet aircraft and the designer of the first jet plane to fly

At half-past four on the morning of 27 August 1939, the telephone's insistent ringing woke Ernst Udet, the top-ranking living ace of the former German Imperial Air Service, and head of the new Luftwaffe's Technical Department.

Udet growled into the phone, still sleepy. The voice from the distance was jubilant. 'This is Heinkel. We've just flown the world's first jet airplane!'

'Fine,' said Udet, grumbling. 'Now let me get back to sleep.'

Germany was only a few days from its invasion of Poland; and Udet could reasonably be expected to be on edge, wondering if each phone call would bring news of the march to the East. But the news that he

Heinkel He 178
Crew: 1 *Powerplant:* 1 Walter R1 liquid-propellant rocket, 100/1000 lb variable thrust
Span: 13·1 ft *Length:* 15·4 ft *Weight:* 4400 lb
Speed: 434 mph at sea level

received in the cool Berlin dawn was electrifying, whether he appreciated its importance or not.

It was, in fact, news of the world's first flight by a jet-propelled gas-turbine powered aircraft, and it was the first step along the path that has led to the supersonic, high-altitude jet fighters of today.

That first aircraft was the Heinkel He 178, a research plane built to serve as a flying test-bed for the new form of powerplant. It was tiny, spanning less than 24 ft and weighing less than two tons, fully loaded with fuel. Its turbojet engine produced about 1000 lb of thrust. Its performance was modest; it probably never flew faster than 350 mph, and never got very far out of sight of the aerodrome at Marienehe. It was overtaken by events. The German Air Ministry ignored it, and eventually it was dropped from active development only a few months after its historic first flight.

In a way, the German Air Ministry couldn't be blamed then for its lack of interest. There were other tasks of a higher priority. Hitler was about to invade Poland, and the air support needed for the job was marginal. If the Polish resistance lasted longer than planned, if the offensive strikes did not knock out enough of the Polish air force, if another country should side with the Poles, there was serious doubt about the ability of the Luftwaffe to maintain its part of the push eastward.

Further, the concept of war held by Hitler and his staff was built around the Blitzkrieg – lightning war – which would move so fast and so powerfully that it would steam-roller the opposition before any countering forces had time to realise what was happening. There was no time for development that might take years to come to fruition. New weapons were needed, yes; but they were needed tomorrow. The jet fighter was an interesting new idea, but of no immediate practical value.

It is not exactly correct to speak of jet propulsion as a new idea. The idea of

propulsion by reaction is as old as propulsion itself. The classical example is the aeolipile, which is supposed to have been demonstrated by the Alexandrian philosopher Hero before the time of Christ. His little sphere, whirled on its bearings by two steam jets driven by the boiling of water inside the sphere, was what we would now call an interesting laboratory experiment. It served to illustrate the principle, but did nothing else.

Jet propulsion was an idea that had to wait for its time to come, primarily because it depended on the generation of high temperatures within an engine. High temperatures and the attendant high pressures required containment in shells that were strong when red-hot. And that required new lightweight metals. True, it could be done with the old ones; steam turbines have been built with traditional metals for the most part. But they are huge and heavy pieces of stationary machinery, hardly suitable for powering aircraft in flight.

And that was the toughest requirement of all. Whatever form of engine was to be built, if it were to fly it had to be light as well as strong. There was no way the jet engine could have been built and flown by the Wright brothers. The state of the art in 1903 simply would not have permitted it.

Jet propulsion is a very general term, because everything that flies under power is propelled by a jet. A propeller, a helicopter rotor, a turbojet or a rocket engine all move an aircraft by jet propulsion. Each of those engines generates a mass of air moving at a higher speed than its surroundings. The difference in momentum is applied as thrust to the airframe, and the aircraft moves through the air, propelled by a jet of faster air.

Toughest problems
The gas turbine for jet propulsion presents some of the toughest design problems ever faced by engineers. The basic problem is to increase the momentum – the mass times the velocity – of the air going through the engine. That is done by burning fuel and adding its energy to that of the incoming air, which is not too difficult to accomplish, in engineering terms. But it is difficult to accomplish with economy of fuel, with safety of operation, and with long life of the moving and stationary parts of the engine.

Building jet engines and getting them to

work was, in retrospect, the simple part. The hard part was getting them to stand up to high performance for hour after hour, while a white-hot exhaust roared out of the tailpipe and the engine glowed from orange to dull red.

The story of today's jet fighters starts, truly, with a young British air cadet, Frank Whittle, studying at the RAF College at Cranwell preparatory to getting his commission. In his fourth term, Whittle wrote a paper, 'Future Developments in Aircraft Design', pointing out some of the possibilities of rockets and of gas turbines driving propellers, but not of the gas turbine producing only a jet of hot air for propulsion.

That came later, about 18 months into his RAF career. Whittle's research had found a basic patent, dated 1917, that covered the principles of jet propulsion for aircraft. Its drawback was obvious; it proposed a piston engine as the power source, driving a fan, or a shrouded propeller within the fuselage, and with the addition of afterburning for additional thrust from the engine.

The principle was sound, but its failings were obvious to Whittle. He hit on the idea of using a gas turbine instead of the piston engine, proposed it to the Air Ministry, and was politely turned down. Materials just didn't exist that could do the job, said the Ministry rejection. Whittle persisted, and filed a patent application for an aircraft gas turbine on 16 January 1930. Because the Air Ministry was not officially interested, the patent was openly published after it was granted about 18 months later. The secret was out.

Another jet pioneer was German aircraft designer Ernst Heinkel, a brilliant innovator. Heinkel was always looking for ways to improve performance, to go faster and higher.

He had become interested in jet propulsion while doing research for an article he was writing in 1935, called 'An Inquiry into Engine Development'. It was a look at future trends desirable for aircraft powerplants. Heinkel saw 500 mph as a practical limit to the speed of propeller-driven aircraft. To get over that hurdle, he reasoned, it would be necessary to have some new kind of propulsion, and he thought in terms of jet engines, primarily those driven by gas turbines.

Late in 1935, Heinkel met Wernher von Braun, then a young engineer testing rocket engines of his own design and longing for an airplane with which to do flight tests. Heinkel loaned von Braun a fuselage from an He 112 fighter, and eventually supported experiments in flight with a modified He 112 driven by an auxiliary rocket engine.

In early 1936, Heinkel's interest was further sparked by a letter from a colleague, Professor Pohl, head of the Science Institute at the University of Göttingen. Pohl's

assistant was a 24-year old scientist named Pabst von Ohain, who had been working on a new kind of aeroplane engine, said Pohl, which did not need a propeller. Pohl believed in the young man and his ideas, and urged Heinkel to investigate.

Heinkel met von Ohain, hired him and his assistant Hahn, and set the team to work in a special building across the aerodrome at Marienehe, a former Mecklenburg state park which Heinkel had bought as the site of a new factory for Luftwaffe production.

Marienehe is rolling country, lying along the Warnow river in the north of Mecklenburg province, now part of the German Democratic Republic. There were farms and estates in the vicinity, and it was a quiet backwater of rural Germany in the years before the war.

But in September 1937 the stillness of the night was disturbed by a low humming that built quickly to a scream and then to a sudden roar. A tongue of flame shot out of the building at the Heinkel field, hot and red, jutting toward the river, scattering the first leaves of fall, lighting the area around the hangar. Von Ohain's strange engine had just been fired for the first time. Hahn telephoned Heinkel with the news, and within a few minutes Heinkel himself was at the building to see and hear the birth of the jet age.

By the next spring the engine was advanced enough to produce repeatable performance. Its fuel was gasoline, instead of the hydrogen used during development work. It produced about 1100 lb of thrust, and it seemed to Heinkel to be ready to power an aircraft.

The design of the aircraft began, with engineers, draftsmen and technicians sworn to secrecy. With that project in capable hands, Heinkel turned back to rocket aircraft, and to experiments aimed at getting one into the air. The first flight of the modified He 112 lent to von Braun's team had been made in April 1937, with the rocket engine operated during flight only. On later tests, pilot Erich Warsitz made takeoffs on the combined power of the He 112's Junkers Jumo piston engine and the von Braun rocket engine in the tail.

Finally, in the summer of 1937, Warsitz made the takeoff on rocket power alone, climbed to altitude, circled the field and landed, using only the rocket engine for propulsion during the entire flight. The point had been proven; Heinkel now was keen to build a special aeroplane for rocket propulsion instead of attempting to modify the He 112 or any other aircraft.

He and Warsitz agreed that the design should aim for the round number of 1000 kilometres per hour speed (621 mph). The airplane was designed around Warsitz. It had a tiny wing span, only 13·1 ft, and the top of the fuselage came up to Warsitz' waist. The nose was detachable in the event

Caproni-Campini N 1
Crew: 2 *Powerplant:* 900 hp Isotta-Fraschini piston engine driving 3-stage ducted fan with afterburner *Span:* 50·3 ft *Length:* 42·9 ft *Weight:* 9229 lb *Speed:* 233 mph at 9800 ft

of an accident, and used a drogue parachute to cut its speed to a point where Warsitz would have been able to bail out and use his own parachute.

Design and construction of the He 176, as the rocket research aircraft was designated, took about one year. It was trucked to the experimental airfield at Peenemünde, later to become world-famous for its development of the A-4 rocket weapon under von Braun. But it was to take another year of slow development before the He 176 was ready for flight. Meanwhile, Warsitz made taxi runs, extending the speed range and distance covered. The Peenemünde runway was lengthened by nearly one mile to accommodate the tests, and Warsitz occasionally took advantage of the long runway to lift the little plane into the air for a few seconds.

Official interference
Meanwhile the Air Ministry did develop some interest in the He 176. They saw it as a potential rocket-powered interceptor, heavily armed and able to slash through bomber formations with great effectiveness. Their insistence on that role for the He 176 caused Heinkel to install small blisters on the fuselage, alleging they were the provisions for armament, but actually filling them with test instrumentation.

Finally Warsitz and the He 176 were ready. On 30 June 1939 the tiny plane blasted off the runway on its first full flight. It lasted less than one minute, but Warsitz and the rest of the Heinkel team were

jubilant. Rocket-powered aircraft had flown before, for short distances and times; but they had been modified aircraft, flying test-beds for the rocket and only a means for getting in-flight data on the powerplant. But none had been considered as a candidate for development into a fighter, although that thought was not exactly uppermost in Heinkel's mind.

On 1 July, Heinkel himself saw the He 176 fly. So did Udet, Milch and others in the Air Ministry. After Warsitz landed, Udet shook his hand and then forbade any further flying with the He 176. 'That's no aeroplane' was his verdict. Warsitz and Heinkel argued for continuance of the tests, and eventually they were successful. Then they were refused permission again. That was rescinded, and permission reinstated, because there was to be a demonstration of new aircraft for Hitler, and the Air Ministry wanted to include the He 176.

Hitler saw it fly, passed a few compliments around, and left the field. Warsitz later had a personal talk with Hitler, during which the subject of the He 176 never came up. Obviously there was to be no official support for the project.

The He 176 and He 178 had been hangar mates, both having been built in a special hangar erected for the purpose away from the rest of the Marienehe plant. Now work concentrated on the He 178, aiming for an early flight.

On the morning of 27 August 1939, Warsitz climbed into the He 178 and started the engine. It whined up to speed; he taxied out, roared down the runway and lifted off. The undercarriage could not be retracted and Warsitz, after trying every trick in the trade, finally resigned himself to circling the field about 1500 ft altitude with the gear hanging. After about six minutes in the air, he swung into the approach pattern, sideslipped on final,' and touched lightly down on the grass, rumbling across the field to a stop.

For Heinkel and the rest of his design team, it was the justification for the hours of work on two pioneering aircraft, both jet-propelled, one by a rocket and one by a gas turbine. Under the circumstances, the Heinkel organisation would have had a tremendous technological lead on the rest of industry. But the events of September 1939 caught up with them. After only a few flights by both airplanes, and despite long hours of arguing, cajoling and pleading by Heinkel, both aircraft projects were stopped

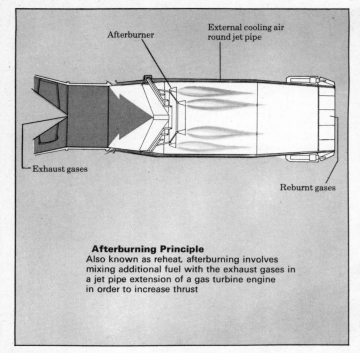

Afterburner

External cooling air round jet pipe

Exhaust gases

Reburnt gases

Afterburning Principle
Also known as reheat, afterburning involves mixing additional fuel with the exhaust gases in a jet pipe extension of a gas turbine engine in order to increase thrust

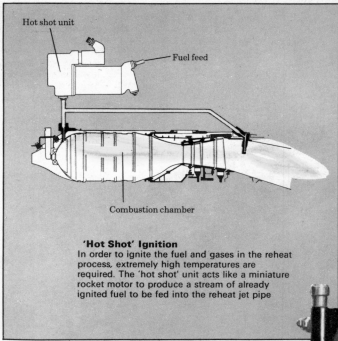

Hot shot unit

Fuel feed

Combustion chamber

'Hot Shot' Ignition
In order to ignite the fuel and gases in the reheat process, extremely high temperatures are required. The 'hot shot' unit acts like a miniature rocket motor to produce a stream of already ignited fuel to be fed into the reheat jet pipe

dead. The word was production, and there was no time for research and development. Besides, they would not be needed for the short war that would be over before winter.

Sadly Heinkel saw both the He 176 and He 178 crated and sent off for display in the Berlin Air Museum. Their fate was predictable from the day they left Marienehe. In 1943, one of the many bombing raids that were to destroy Berlin pounded the Air Museum and its priceless collection of aeronautical history into rubble.

Soon after the pioneering flights of the two Heinkel jet-propelled aircraft in 1939, an Italian research aircraft flew from Milan to Rome under jet power. It was the first cross-country flight of any length by a jet-propelled aircraft, and even though the run included a stop for fuel, the flight was epochal.

The airplane was the Caproni-Campini N 1, a low-winged monoplane with a cylindrical fuselage. A circular inlet at the nose and an exhaust nozzle at the tail gave the only clues to the internal arrangement, which was unusual. In some ways, it predated the most advanced jet engines operational today; but it was then only a makeshift approach to jet propulsion.

Inside the N 1, an Isotta-Fraschini piston engine, which developed about 900 hp, drove a three-stage variable-pitch fan in an application of the principle of the ducted fan, today the most economical and advanced type of turbojet development. Downstream of the ducted fan discharge was a ring burner fed with fuel to augment the thrust of the engine-driven fan; it was, in essence, an afterburner.

Designer Secondo Campini had been working on the idea of a jet-propelled aeroplane for eight years, and had hit upon this particular scheme, perhaps as a result of finding earlier research and patents along this line.

The N 1 made its first flight on 27 August 1940 from Forlanini aerodrome near Milan, and was airborne for about ten minutes. The cross-country flight to Rome was basically a ferry flight to get the aircraft to the Italian aeronautical test establishment at Guidonia. With maximum publicity planned, the N 1 took off from Forlanini and headed south. A fuelling stop was made at Pisa, and the final landing at Rome.

It was found to be a not very efficient method of achieving jet propulsion. The programme was abandoned about two years after the first flight, although Campini continued to press for adoption of his basic ideas as a possible auxiliary powerplant for fighter aircraft.

Flight International

Frank Whittle, British pioneer of jet aircraft who patented his first jet engine in 1930

THE WHITTLE ENGINE

Whittle W 1 Turbojet: 2-sided centrifugal compressor, 10 reverse-flow interconnected combustion chambers *Fuel:* Paraffin with atomised burners *Specific fuel consumption:* 1·4 lb/lb thrust/hour *Performance:* 850 lb static thrust at 16,500 rpm *Thrust/Weight ratio:* 1:0·66

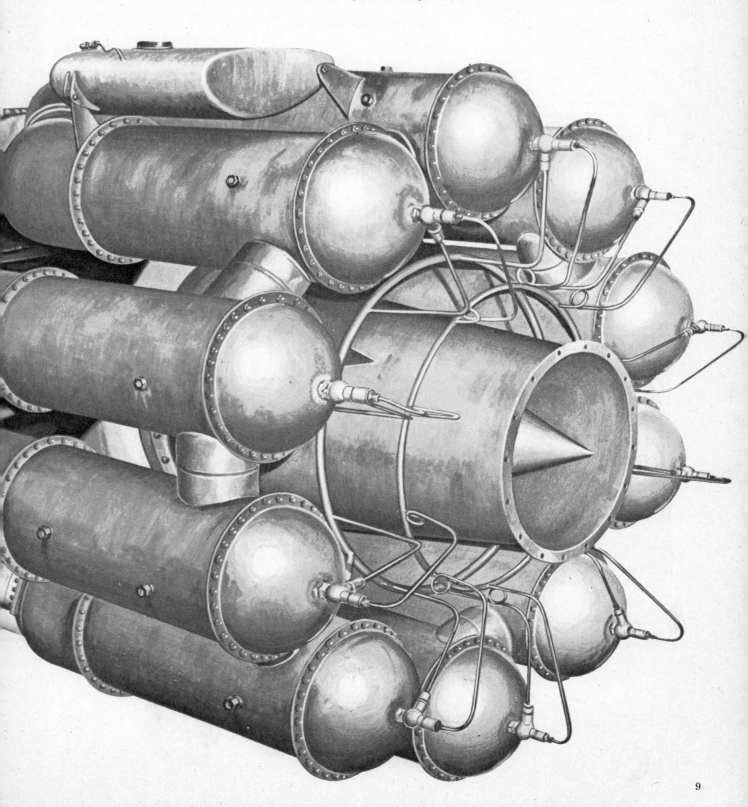

The early experiments with jet engines and aircraft led to both Britain and Germany having jet fighters operational during the Second World War. Me 262s terrorised British bombers, while Gloster Meteors brought down several V-1 flying bombs. But against conventional aircraft the jet planes' superior speed could also be a handicap, hindering accurate fire

TOO FAST TO FIGHT

The real impetus to the development of jet aircraft was the start of the Second World War in September 1939. As country after country realised the ugly truth, industry, science and engineering teams girded for their parts in the struggle to come.

Germany had a head start, thanks to the pioneering work by Ernst Heinkel. So it should not be surprising that the world's first turbojet aircraft to be designed as a fighter from the beginning was yet another Heinkel effort, the He 280. It was also the world's first twin-jet aircraft.

Heinkel visualised a twin-engined jet fighter, with engines slung in individual nacelles under the wing, minimising the length of the intake and exhaust ducting. For ground clearance, and to avoid blasting loose huge chunks of the runway surface, he decided on tricycle landing gear, the first on a German aircraft.

Design of the He 280 started in late 1939. In March 1940, the Air Ministry awarded a contract to the Messerschmitt organisation for prototypes of a twin-engined aircraft. A few days later, Heinkel got essentially the same sort of contract.

The first prototype He 280 was completed by September, lacking only airworthy engines. Heinkel had the prototype flown first as a glider, testing basic aerodynamic characteristics. When the Heinkel HeS 8A engines were ready for flight the following spring, the airplane was already well understood.

On 2 April 1941, at Marienehe airfield, Fritz Schaefer climbed into the cockpit of the He 280. He taxied out and took off, climbing to 900 ft or so for a circle of the field. He did not attempt to retract the landing gear, or to do anything exceptional with the aircraft.

Three days later it was flown again, and demonstrated to Udet and others from the Air Ministry. Their indifference was annoying to Heinkel, who could not understand why his advanced ideas were continually rejected.

He thought the He 280 had proved its point and that it should be considered for production. So he arranged a series of tests against the Luftwaffe's top fighter of the time, the Focke-Wulf 190. It was no contest; the jet-propelled fighter outperformed the Fw 190 in every way. The Ministry bent a little, and awarded Heinkel a contract for 13 pre-production aircraft.

His designers put together a further development, with the unusually heavy armament of six 20-mm cannon, and proposed it to the Air Ministry. To everybody's surprise, the Ministry awarded a contract for the production of 300, but Heinkel's facilities, strained as they were by existing production programmes, were bypassed by this order and the He 280 was scheduled to be built by another firm.

But by then the Me 262 had flown under jet power; it appeared so promising that the Ministry cancelled the He 280.

The rocket-powered jet fighter arrived, in prototype form, in 1941. On 13 August Messerschmitt test pilot Heini Dittmar strapped himself into a prototype Me 163A, started the rocket engine, and blasted across the turf at Peenemünde-West, the experimental Luftwaffe airfield. The Me 163A was held in a climb until the fuel was burned; then Dittmar turned and began a circling letdown to a landing. It was the first flight by a rocket-powered interceptor prototype, and it began a long, frustrating and ultimately unsuccessful development programme.

It had begun some years earlier, as a project to power a tailless glider designed by Dr Alexander Lippisch. Working at the German Research Institute for Soaring (DFS), Lippisch's team had brought along the design of their DFS 194 to the point where it obviously required industrial support.

Messerschmitt was designated, and Lippisch's team went to Augsburg. The aircraft turned out well, but its rocket powerplant did not, and the DFS 194 was never flown under power. It was used instead for ground tests of the rocket.

The baulky rocket was replaced by a new design with controllable thrust, other changes were made, and the result was the Me 163A series, prototypes used for development of the interceptor version.

It was one of this first batch of 13 that Dittmar first flew in August 1941. But there was a long time between that first flight and the first operational sortie. The Me 163 did not see action until 13 May 1944, and even that attempt to seek combat was made in a development aircraft, one of the Me 163B prototypes. By the time the Luftwaffe had had production versions of the Me 163B in service, the war was running down and the visions of hundreds of the tiny rocket fighters slashing through disrupted bomber formations had been reduced to the actual-

Messerschmitt Me 163
Crew: 1 *Powerplant:* 1 Walter RII liquid-propellant rocket *Span:* 30·5 ft *Length:* 17·8 ft *Weight:* 5291 lb *Speed:* 558 mph

MOD

ity of a few sporadic intercepts and some hideous operational accidents.

A dispassionate examination of the concept led to one conclusion: it was possible to be too fast for effective combat. The Me 163s were designed to be used as interceptors of daylight bombing raids. They were to take off and climb rapidly (they could get to bomber height in less than three minutes), attack the bombers with their paired 30-mm cannon, and break away for the return to base.

In practice, the speed of the rocket fighter was so much greater than that of

its bomber target that a pilot only had two or three seconds to aim and fire. It proved to be nearly impossible. The Me 163 was not suitable for combat against slow-flying bombers.

Those that did get into combat managed to shoot down a few bombers, but it was too late. The factory producing one of the essential fuel components was bombed in

May 1973: 'Vintage Pair' of the RAF's Historic Flight, a De Havilland Vampire T 11, the last Vampire still flying with the RAF, and a Gloster Meteor T 7.

August 1944. Ground transportation was under constant attack, and several complete shipments of rocket fuel were lost to Allied gunnery. As winter neared, the weather worsened – and the Me 163 was not suitable for bad weather or night operations. The whole programme ground to a halt, with only a few intercepts flown against special targets such as high-altitude photo flights.

There was only one truly successful jet fighter developed and brought to operational status during the Second World War: the Messerschmitt Me 262. In spite of setbacks to the smooth development of the programme caused by such diverse factors as Hitler's dreams and bombing realities, the project maintained and even gained momentum.

It began in late 1938 with an Air Ministry contract with Messerschmitt for a twin-engine jet fighter. By March 1940, both Messerschmitt and Heinkel were told to go ahead with the development of their respective twin-jet fighters.

The first Messerschmitt prototype was completed well before its jet engines were ready for flight. The first alternative, to fit

rocket engines in the nacelles for flight tests, was ruled out because the engines weren't considered safe enough.

So Messerschmitt installed a standard Junkers Jumo piston engine in the nose, and the first flight of an Me 262 was made on 18 April 1941, with a piston engine and propeller providing propulsion, and empty jet nacelles under the wings. By March of the following year airworthy jet engines were available, and on 25 March the prototype was flown on the combined power of its piston engine and the two new jets. It nearly ended in disaster for the pilot, Fritz Wendel, because both turbojets failed shortly after takeoff, and he had a tough time keeping the Me 262 in the air.

Wendel made the first flight on jet power only with the third prototype, which had been fitted with a pair of Junkers Jumo 004A-0 turbojets producing about 1850 lb of thrust each. On 18 July 1942 he took off from the hard-surfaced runway at Leipheim for a flight of about twelve minutes. He completed a second flight that day, and was delighted with the way the plane handled.

But he had had to use brakes momentarily during the takeoff roll, in order to get the tail up into the slipstream so that the elevators would be effective. The braking served to rotate the aircraft nose down and had to be done carefully, gently and at exactly the right time.

This must have been one of the reasons that Messerschmitt decided to redesign the Me 262 with a new type of landing gear – the tricycle type with nosewheel – that became the standard for all subsequent Me 262s.

Happily for the Allied cause, the decision-making machinery broke down on the Me 262 programme. Production schedules were changed almost monthly. Variations on the theme were developed on request and the Me 262 was built as a fighter, an all-weather fighter, a reconnaissance aircraft, a ground-attack aircraft, a fighter with reconnaissance capabilities, a fighter-bomber, and an interceptor with rocket booster engines in the nacelles, all in a single-seat version. Two-seat models were developed as trainers and night fighters. They were built in small batches of only a few of most of the versions, and only one model was produced in any quantity.

It was July 1944 before the Me 262 engaged in combat, the first recorded instance being an encounter with a reconnaissance Mosquito flown by Flt Lt Wall, RAF. Wall reported that an Me 262 made five passes at his Mosquito, but in each case he was able to break away and finally dove into clouds to escape his persistent adversary.

Time and the losing position of Germany caught up with the Me 262. By tremendous industrial effort, mass production of the aircraft had been achieved under mountains of difficulties. The first production aircraft had been delivered in March 1944, and by February 1945 production had peaked at 300 completed aircraft per month. Factory delivery data show that 1320 were rolled out of the doors for delivery to the Luftwaffe during the 13-month production programme.

The most famous unit to operate the Me 262 was JV 44, formed and commanded by General Adolf Galland. The unit arrived

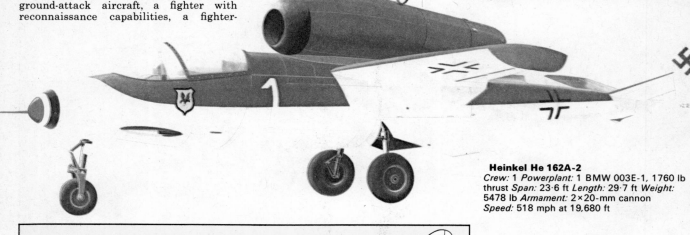

Heinkel He 162A-2
Crew: 1 *Powerplant:* 1 BMW 003E-1, 1760 lb thrust *Span:* 23·6 ft *Length:* 29·7 ft *Weight:* 5478 lb *Armament:* 2×20-mm cannon *Speed:* 518 mph at 19,680 ft

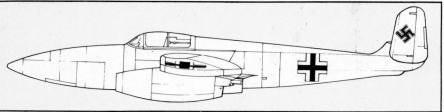

Cockpit is a totally enclosed unit for pressurisation purposes, although no service machines were ever pressurised

Heinkel He 280
Crew: 1 *Powerplant:* 2 HeS 8, 1100 lb thrust each *Span:* 40 ft *Length:* 34·1 ft *Weight:* 9500 lb *Armament:* 3×20-mm cannon *Speed:* 558 mph at 19,680 ft

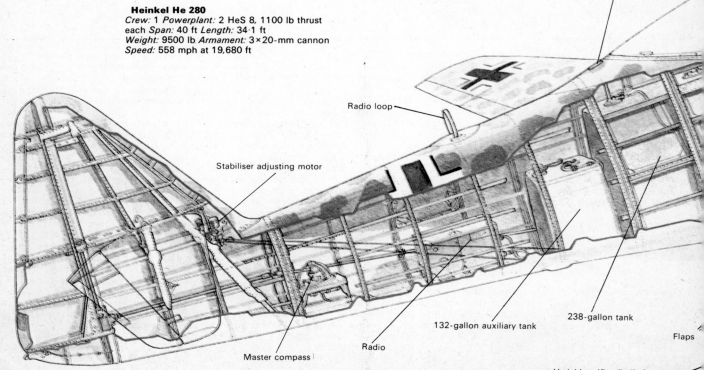

Tank filler cap

Radio loop

Stabiliser adjusting motor

Master compass

Radio

132-gallon auxiliary tank

238-gallon tank

Flaps

Variable orifice 'bullet' moves in and out to vary exit area

at its base near Munich on the last day of March 1945, and operated for only about one month, finally making its sorties from the autobahn between Munich and Augsburg. But in that time, they terrorised bomber crews, made about 50 kills, and established once and for all the value of the jet fighter.

As Germany's position grew more desperate, so did attempts to develop new weapons to stave off the inevitable. One of these was the Heinkel 162, a tricky single-engined jet fighter. Its specification, issued in September 1944, called for a lightweight fighter, using an absolute minimum of strategic materials, and capable of being put into rapid mass production. It was to be flown into combat by the loyal Hitler Youth,

after they had been given a brief training period on gliders.

Heinkel was awarded the contract on 30 September. By 29 October the He 162 had been designed, and construction had begun. The first prototype was flown on 6 December, with Flugkapitän Peter at the controls. One month later, the first He 162s were delivered to a test unit, and in February 1945 I/JG-1 began conversion to the type.

Few German records remain of those frantic last days, but there is at least one reported incident of combat between an He 162 and a USAAF P-51 Mustang. The jet was able to turn and climb with the Mustang, but it was much faster and had greater acceleration. The combat was inconclusive; neither claimed victory.

By the end of the war, about 275 had been built and another 800 were in various stages of assembly. It was a formidable accomplishment by the Heinkel organisation. They designed a contemporary jet fighter in one month, flew it nine weeks after starting design, and delivered 275 in less than seven months.

There was one more last-gasp defence effort to fly: the Bachem 349 Natter. Work had begun in the spring of 1944, to a specification for a target defence interceptor. Bachem's first proposal was rejected in

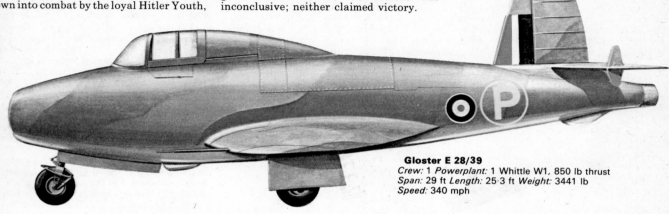

Gloster E 28/39
Crew: 1 *Powerplant:* 1 Whittle W1, 850 lb thrust *Span:* 29 ft *Length:* 25·3 ft *Weight:* 3441 lb *Speed:* 340 mph

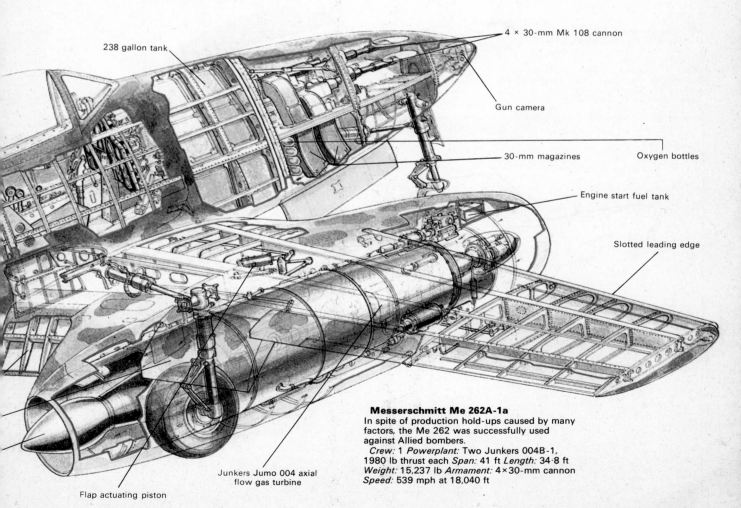

238 gallon tank

4 × 30-mm Mk 108 cannon

Gun camera

30-mm magazines

Oxygen bottles

Engine start fuel tank

Slotted leading edge

Messerschmitt Me 262A-1a
In spite of production hold-ups caused by many factors, the Me 262 was successfully used against Allied bombers.
Crew: 1 *Powerplant:* Two Junkers 004B-1, 1980 lb thrust each *Span:* 41 ft *Length:* 34·8 ft *Weight:* 15,237 lb *Armament:* 4×30-mm cannon *Speed:* 539 mph at 18,040 ft

Junkers Jumo 004 axial flow gas turbine

Flap actuating piston

favour of a Heinkel design; but Erich Bachem knew the sources of power and had an interview with Heinrich Himmler. The decision of the Ministry was immediately changed to support the Bachem proposal as well.

It was a tiny wooden airframe powered by a single rocket engine, boosted by four solid-propellant rockets, launched from a vertical tower, and armed by a nose full of air-to-air rockets. The attack over, the pilot was expected to bail out. He and the valuable engine were to be saved by parachutes.

The Natter was tested as a glider in November 1944, launched unmanned in December under boost power only, and was successful in both tests. But the first piloted flight ended in disaster. On 28 February 1945 Oberleutnant Lothar Siebert, a volunteer for the test flight, was killed when the canopy came off during launch, ap-

parently knocking him unconscious as it left. The Natter crashed out of control. But the next three manned launches were successful, and the programme moved ahead. Seven manned flights were made in all, and the production programme continued to grind out the wooden airframes which took only a few hundred man-hours each to build.

In April 1945, a squadron of 10 Natters was set up ready to launch near Stuttgart, waiting for the next bomber raid for its initiation into combat. But before the aerial assault, Allied armoured units rolled into the area, and the Natter crews destroyed their aircraft to keep them from falling into enemy hands. That was the effective end of the Natter programme.

The turbulence of war was a major factor in the establishment and cancellation of aircraft programmes. It was the beginning of war that must have been one of the events prompting the issuing of a British Air Ministry specification, E 28/39, for a single-seat fighter prototype aircraft powered by a gas turbine for jet propulsion.

Earlier, the Ministry had contracted with Power Jets, a firm headed by Frank Whittle, for development of an airworthy jet engine. Power Jets received its first Ministry support in March 1938; the engine contract was received on 7 July 1939.

The aircraft contract, issued to Gloster Aircraft on 3 February 1940, described a design based on the need for an interceptor. Top speed was to be about 380 mph, and armament was to be four machine-guns. The primary purpose of the aircraft was to obtain flight data on the engine, but it was also to be a prototype fighter.

The first run of an engine in the E 28/39 airframe was made on 6 April 1941, using an unairworthy engine. The next day, Flt Lt P E G Sayer began taxi tests at Brockworth. The plane rolled across the green field, picking up speed and slowing again as Sayer felt out the handling. Three times during the taxi runs, Sayer lifted the plane off the ground briefly. It seemed ready to fly.

The first prototype was trucked to the airfield at Cranwell, home of the RAF College where Whittle had spent his cadet days. There were practical as well as sentimental reasons for selecting that field. It had a long runway, with clear approaches, and was one of the best available fields for test work.

On 14 May Sayer repeated some of the taxi tests and planned to fly the following day. Low clouds hid the sky on the morning of May 15, but towards evening they began to lift. The camouflaged E 28/39 with Sayer in the cockpit trundled out to the starting area. There was a rising howl from the

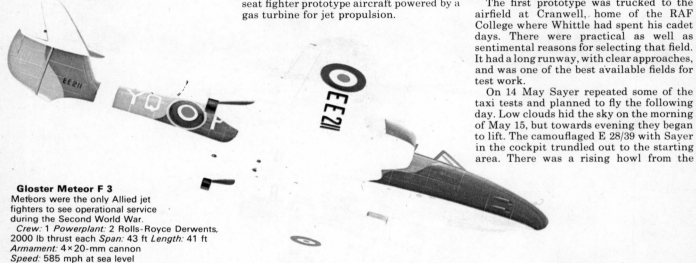

Gloster Meteor F 3
Meteors were the only Allied jet fighters to see operational service during the Second World War.
  Crew: 1 *Powerplant:* 2 Rolls-Royce Derwents, 2000 lb thrust each *Span:* 43 ft *Length:* 41 ft
Armament: 4 × 20-mm cannon
Speed: 585 mph at sea level

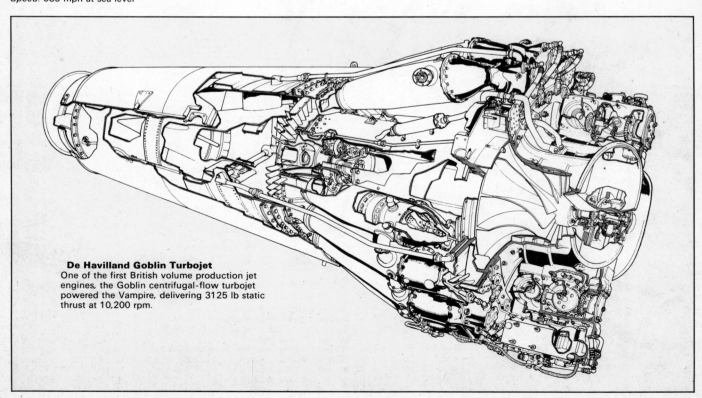

De Havilland Goblin Turbojet
One of the first British volume production jet engines, the Goblin centrifugal-flow turbojet powered the Vampire, delivering 3125 lb static thrust at 10,200 rpm.

engine, the plane began to move, and with darkness already gathering, Sayer lifted the plane off on its first flight.

He stayed aloft 17 minutes. It was the first flight ever made by a British jet-propelled aircraft.

Official support came soon. The flight programme was pushed to learn more about this new form of propulsion. Gradually the aircraft was taken to 25,000 ft and 300 mph in less than 10 hours flying.

Later, Rolls-Royce took over development of the engine, and raised its basic thrust to 1400 lb. Then the plane was flown to a maximum speed of 466 mph, and to an altitude above 42,000 ft. Gloster completed its portion of the programme in late June 1943, and turned the E 28/39 over to the care of the Royal Aircraft Establishment at Farnborough.

Britain's first true jet fighter was the Gloster Meteor, begun as an answer to specification F 9/40. It was planned as a twin-engine craft, because one engine of the type then available was hardly sufficient to obtain performance better than that of contemporary piston-engined fighters. Further, there was a supposed advantage of twin-engine reliability and safety.

The Gloster design team laid out their twin with the jet engines buried in the wings, and with the rear spars built around large holes for the jet pipes to pass through. Tricycle landing gear and a high tail were other basic decisions. Armament was to be four 20-mm cannon in the nose, and the cockpit was to be pressurised. Design began some time around August 1940.

About a year later, problems arose with the specified engines; the Power Jets W 2B engines had not been declared airworthy. One prototype was converted to take the Halford H 1 engines then in advanced development, and another to take the Metropolitan-Vickers F 2 engines. The H 1 engines were first cleared for flight, and the fifth prototype Meteor was trucked to the aerodrome at Cranwell, where Gloster pilot Michael Daunt made the first flight on 5 March 1943.

With Rolls-Royce in the engine programme, the final choice for the Meteor powerplant was the Welland W 2B, basically the Whittle/Power Jets engine. Wellands powered the first 20 production F Mk 1 Meteors, a fighter rushed into production

and action near the end of the war. Issued to 616 Squadron RAF, based at Culmhead and later at Manston, they first saw action on 27 July 1944, on 'Diver' patrol against the German V-1 buzz-bombs. Sqdn Ldr Watts was the first Meteor pilot to contact one; but his guns jammed and the flying bomb continued on course. First kill of a V-1 was made on 4 August by F/O Dean, whose guns also jammed. So Dean closed the distance, eased the Meteor's wingtip under that of the V-1, and banked sharply away. The Meteor's wingtip slammed against the V-1's wing and sent it into a spiral dive and a crash in open country.

F/O Rogers, almost at the same time, was having more conventional success. His guns fired, and he became the first RAF pilot to shoot down an enemy aircraft from a jet fighter.

Britain's only other jet fighter of the war years, the de Havilland DH 100 Vampire, was very different from the Meteor. Designed to specification E 6/41, which defined an experimental aircraft rather than

the fighter required by the Gloster Meteor specification of F 9/40, the Vampire started to take shape on the drawing boards at Hatfield in May 1942.

The single jet engine was enclosed in an egg-shaped fuselage, with inlets for the air at the root of each wing, and the exhaust discharging directly aft on the centre line of the egg. De Havilland designers used twin tail booms, perhaps borrowing the idea from the piston-engined Lockheed P-38 Lightning.

The Vampire was all metal, but there was one holdover from earlier DH designs; the cockpit section was constructed of a plywood and balsa sandwich material.

It was an all-DH project. The engine was the Halford H 1, designed by Maj Frank Halford and built by de Havilland. Geoffrey de Havilland, Jr, made the first flight on 30 September 1943, at Hatfield, six months after the Meteor had flown. The time differential was critical; the Meteor just barely saw action near the end of the war, but the Vampire was too late to be tested under combat conditions.

About a year earlier, the first flight of the first US jet fighter, the Bell XP-59A, had taken place. The site was a remote desert area, part of the USAAF Muroc Bombing and Gunnery Range located on a dry lake bed about 100 miles north of Los Angeles, California. (That site later became Edwards Air Force Base.)

Robert M Stanley, then chief pilot for Bell, fired up the twin General Electric I-A turbojets, which had been closely but not completely copied from the British W 2B engines. A few minutes later, on the after-

De Havilland Vampire F 1
Crew: 1 *Powerplant:* DH Goblin, 3125 lb thrust
Span: 40 ft *Length:* 30·8 ft
Armament: 4×20-mm cannon
Speed: 525 mph at 25,000 ft

noon of 1 October 1942, the XP-59A lifted off the dry lake bed into the California sky.

It would not have made such progress without British help. Major General Henry H Arnold, then Chief of the USAAC, visited Britain in the spring of 1941, saw the Whittle engine and the E 28/39, and was impressed. After follow-up meetings, it was agreed that the US should copy the Whittle engine and develop a twin-engine fighter around it. Bell were chosen as the airframe company to be responsible, and General Electric were chosen to build the engines. Bell were given eight months from the date of the contract approval to have their first aircraft ready for flight.

Construction stayed on schedule, but the timetable for GE engine deliveries slipped. They were not ready until August 1942, and they were never trouble-free. Their performance did not meet expectations, because

Smithsonian Institution Photo No A516A

Bell XP-59A Airacomet
More of a research aircraft than a service fighter, the XP-59A first flew in October 1942

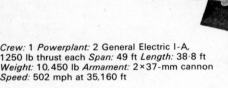

Crew: 1 *Powerplant:* 2 General Electric I-A, 1250 lb thrust each *Span:* 49 ft *Length:* 38·8 ft *Weight:* 10,450 lb *Armament:* 2×37-mm cannon *Speed:* 502 mph at 35,160 ft

the British data used as the basis for their design proved optimistic. Neither the original nor later production engines ever developed the predicted thrust. Consequently, the P-59 Airacomet never served with front-line units; it served instead with a squadron training pilots and mechanics on the new aircraft.

It was obvious early in the Bell programme that its performance was not going to be earth-shaking. Everybody had ideas about what to do, but Lockheed's Clarence L (Kelly) Johnson was to see his ideas take tangible form.

Lockheed had done earlier work on a jet fighter proposal, had been rejected, but had persisted. On one of Johnson's periodic visits to Wright Field, then the technical headquarters of the USAAF, he was asked to consider designing a jet fighter around a British engine. Within a few days the first sketches were ready, and Johnson got the go-ahead in June 1943. At the far side of the Lockheed airport at Burbank, California, a temporary building was erected, the 'Skunk Works', named after a mythical factory in the popular comic strip, 'Li'l Abner'.

The contract gave Lockheed 180 days to design, build and fly the XP-80. They beat the construction deadline and had the plane ready to go in 143 days. But the first flight was delayed by engine availability, and it was not until 9 January 1943, that Lockheed chief test pilot Milo Burcham made the first flight with the XP-80 from the dry lake bed at Muroc.

Then Lockheed had to repeat the whole performance. It was decided that the production P-80 would be powered by the new General Electric I-40 engine, based on British designs. Back to the Skunk Works went Johnson's team, to emerge 139 days later with another prototype, the XP-80A. It first flew on 11 June 1944, and by the time the war ended, 45 had been delivered to USAAF squadrons. A few had even been tested at operational bases in England and Italy, but had been kept from any area where combat might have been possible.

Early in the development of the jet fighter, the navies of Great Britain and the US had studied the new type and wondered how best to adapt it to carrier operations. In the US, the Navy Bureau of Aeronautics were sponsoring the development of a series of axial-flow turbojets by Westinghouse Electric Corp. These small-diameter engines promised much better overall installed performance than did the bulkier centrifugal-flow engines pioneered by Whittle, Rolls-Royce, and General Electric.

The Navy, Westinghouse and the McDonnell Aircraft Corp got together in early 1943 to discuss the design of a Naval fighter built around two or more of the Westinghouse engines. McDonnell designers investigated a wide range of possibilities, guided by basically conservative design policies. They checked eight-, six-, four- and twin-engined schemes and settled on the twin as the basis for their design of the XFD-1. It was to be a fighter

with a defensive mission of combat air patrol at 15,000 ft above a carrier task force. Two years and a few days after the contract was signed, the first prototype XFD-1 took to the air on 26 January 1945. Two months later McDonnell received a production order.

But the war was to be over by almost two years when the first McDonnell Phantoms, redesignated FH-1, were delivered to the fleet. By then, it was apparent that the Phantoms were only an interim type serving to accumulate some fleet experience with jet fighters.

To the East, the Russians had been working for several years to develop their own rocket-powered interceptor. Two designers – Bereznyak and Isaev – planned a tiny aircraft around a single rocket engine rated at 2420 lb of thrust. They designed a conventional fighter, armed with a pair of 20-mm cannon in the nose, and intended for the same kind of mission as the Me 163.

The expected bomber raids against Russia never happened; the rocket-powered interceptor would not have been needed. But it was a fatal accident during a test flight that put an end to the development programme. The first flight had been successful. Test pilot Grigori Bakhchivandzhe flew the BI for a little longer than three minutes on its maiden trip on 15 May 1942.

It was slow development. A second plane was added, but the rocket engine proved troublesome. Only six flights were logged in ten months. Bakhchivandzhe was killed

Smithsonian Institution Photo No 75-Y844

Lockheed XP-80 Shooting Star
The USAF's first service jet, modelled on British Whittle designs, arrived too late to see combat. The sectional diagram (below left) shows the layout of the cockpit, engine and fuselage construction
Crew: 1 *Powerplant:* 1 Halford H-1, 2460 lb thrust *Span:* 36·9 ft *Length:* 32·8 ft
Weight: 8916 lb *Speed:* 502 mph at 20,480 ft

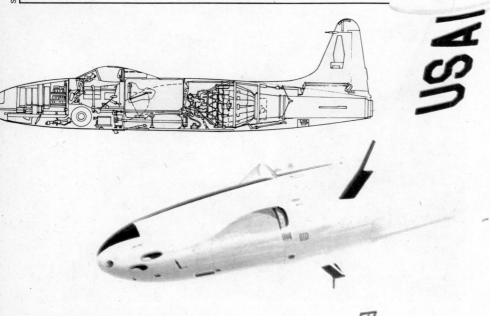

One of only two wartime jet fighter programmes to get under way in Japan, the Mitsubishi J8M1 Shusui was little more than a copy of an Me 163 in Japanese markings

Maru Magazine/Orion Press

on the seventh, a high-speed run at relatively low altitude. Witnesses saw black smoke instead of the usual short red-orange flame from the engine; the plane pitched down and began to disintegrate in the air before it crashed and exploded.

The seven airframes that had been built were scrapped along with the components for another 20 or so, on orders from the Kremlin banning all further work on rocket fighters.

Only two jet fighter projects ever got under way in Japan, and both were inspired by German developments. Japan acquired licence rights to the Me 163 and its rocket engine. But delivery of a sample Me 163 and a complete set of blueprints was not completed; the submarine carrying them to Japan was sunk. Japan received only a single rocket engine and an Me 163 manual a Japanese naval officer had brought back from a visit to Germany.

In July 1944 the Japanese Navy issued a specification for a rocket-powered interceptor. The Army joined the programme, and the first prototype of a training glider was completed by December 1944. It flew successfully, after being towed to altitude and released. But the aircraft itself, the Mitsubishi J8M1, was not as successful. The first prototype was finished in June 1945, and its first flight was scheduled for 7 July. The engine failed soon after takeoff, and the J8M1 smashed into the ground, killing Lt Cdr Toyohiko Inuzuka, the test pilot. Although production had started,

and other J8M1 aircraft were available, no more flights were made before the Japanese surrender.

The success of the Me 262 programme sparked Japanese interest in a twin-jet fighter, and the Navy issued an order to Nakajima for development of such a fighter, based on the German twin-jet craft but smaller. Data were limited. The turbojet engines were designed using, among other

sources, photographs of the German BMW 003 turbojet. The first prototype was completed in August 1945, just days before the final bell rang for Japan. On 7 August it made its first flight from the Naval air base at Kisarazu, with Lt Cdr Susumu Tanaoha at the controls. On his second flight, Tanaoha had to abort during the takeoff run because of engine failure. It was the last attempt to fly the Nakajima J8N1 *Kikka*.

Britain and Germany were the first countries to develop jet fighters. Unfortunately, Britain was slow to adapt to the development of jet aircraft technology. The USA and USSR adopted the axial flow engine and sweptback wing configuration (both based on German research) much earlier: seizing the lead in the postwar years, they never let it go

The victorious Allied armies that steamrollered through Germany towards the end of the Second World War liberated filing cabinets and desk drawers crammed with documents on aerodynamic, structural and powerplant ideas, designs and tests. It was a bonanza, a major foundation for the postwar development of jet fighters.

In spite of the intense pressures of war, German scientists working in university and government research institutes were able to develop ideas at their own pace. They had time to calculate, sketch, build models and test them in flight or a wind tunnel. Combined with practical experience from operational use of a wide variety of unusual weapons and aircraft, this wealth of data fell almost intact into Allied hands at the end of the war.

Many of these ideas had been discovered or developed earlier by scientists in other countries. But in Great Britain and the United States, there was more pressure to produce aircraft in quantity than there was to improve the breed with new and revolutionary ideas, even though both countries did develop and produce jet fighters during the war. But they did not do so on the scale of Germany, and their operational experience was very limited compared to that of the Luftwaffe.

One major contribution made by the Germans was their standardisation of axial-flow jet engines of reduced diameters, compared to the centrifugal-flow types pioneered by Heinkel and Whittle. The axial-flow jets were better suited to installation in a slim fighter fuselage, or under the wings. It took several postwar years before other nations realised that the axial-flow engine was really the best way to do the job.

Another German contribution was sweepback. Known as early as 1935, sweepback reduces the drag of the wing by aerodynamically thinning the wing section. German wind tunnel tests proved and evaluated this, and almost every late wartime German design featured a sweptback wing.

The combination of these two basic concepts – the axial-flow engine and sweepback – produced a long series of combat aircraft after the war, spilled over into civilian designs in the late 1950s, and remains as the basic configuration of many military and civil aircraft today.

The Germans spent a tremendous amount of their scientific resources on guided missiles. Even though they were not all applicable to fighter design, or to exploitation for fighter use, the basic technology developed for them furnished valuable background experience.

Unguided missiles and air-to-air rockets were developed and used operationally by

Smithsonian Institution Photo No 75-Y843

The Republic XF-91 mixed-powerplant (rocket and turbojet) sweptwing interceptor

POSTWAR DEVELOPMENTS

THE SWEEP TOWARDS MACH 1

the Germans, and that type of weapon was destined to become an important part of the striking power of fighters to come.

Airborne radar systems, primitive though they were, had been used by both sides during the war. Postwar, they blossomed as technology advanced. Combined with ground-based long-range radars and improved communications, they formed the beginnings of the highly effective command and control systems now in operation.

Gradually these developments began to come together. A new design might evaluate one or two new ideas; later designs might add a third or fourth. And, piece by piece, the unsophisticated jets of the war's end built to advanced designs that broke through the speed of sound, and could fly and fight in an all-weather environment.

Those few postwar years were exciting. There was money to spend on unusual concepts, and designers had a wealth of data to draw on. The jet fighters we talk about here are only those that were

significant during that period. For every one of these, there were others that led only to a dead end in development.

During the five years between the end of the Second World War and the start of the Korean conflict, the design lead was seized and exploited by the United States and Russia, and they have never let go of it. The British, whose truly pioneering efforts contributed so much to the early development of the jet fighter, never exploited their position with advanced technology. They stayed too long with the straight wing and the centrifugal engine and – with one exception – never again became a technological competitor in fighter design.

This period of time also saw the emergence of strong jet fighter design teams in France and Sweden. Both countries continued to improve their position, the French more rapidly and on a broader scale because of their greater size and wealth. Today they stand on a technical par with the United

States and Russia in advanced aeronautics.

28 February 1946:
Republic XP-84 Thunderjet
This American aircraft was the first significant jet fighter to fly in the postwar years. Sleek, powered by a new General Electric axial-flow engine, the XP-84 was designed as an interceptor, but was destined to spend most of its long career in the USAF as a fighter-bomber. It was later blooded in the Korean war, and was the mainstay of tactical airpower for many Allied countries and the United States during the years of cold war.

24 April 1946:
Yakovlev Yak-15 and Mikoyan MiG-9
Both these Russian jet fighters, first of that country's postwar types to fly, were powered by originals or copies of German jet engines that had been captured in quantity by the Russians. The Yak-15 was a single-engined modification of a piston-engined interceptor that saw much service during the war. It was the first of the pair to fly, followed into the air within minutes by the MiG-9, a bulkier, twin-engined fighter. Both types went into production, although the MiG-9 faded from the scene early and the Yak-15 stayed on in service in Russia and some of its allied countries, and was later developed further.

27 July 1946:
Supermarine Attacker
This was the first jet fighter to serve with the Royal Navy on carriers, but it had started life as a land-based interceptor design for the Royal Air Force. Developed late in the war years, it was built around

the ubiquitous centrifugal-flow engine and a straight wing adapted from the last of the piston-engined Spitfire line. With the Attacker, the Royal Navy learned the operational problems of jet fighters.

11 November 1946:
SNCASO 6000-01 Triton
French daring developed their first jet aircraft, designed under the noses of occupying German troops. Work began in 1943, in spite of the lack of contact with other countries developing jet aircraft, the systematic despoiling of the industry and German labour drafts that decimated its personnel. The Triton was a single-engined test-bed, built to be able to handle a variety of jet engines. The first prototype flew – on the anniversary of Armistice Day – under the power of a German jet Junkers 004B. It was the harbinger of dynamic French fighter designs to come.

27 November 1944:
North American XFJ-1 Fury
This stubby, straight-winged aircraft was North America's first jet fighter. It was designed as one of two successors to the Navy's first jet, the McDonnell Phantom, and was bought only in small quantity because other and newer developments were coming along rapidly. It served with only one squadron on one carrier, and might have been forgotten but for one thing: its rugged airframe was the basis that led to NAA's sweptwing XP-86 the following year.

11 January 1947:
McDonnell XF2H-1 Banshee
A bigger and more powerful brother-in-arms to the Phantom then in fleet service with the US Navy, the Banshee was a linear, almost scaled-up development of the earlier McDonnell jet fighter. It had more of

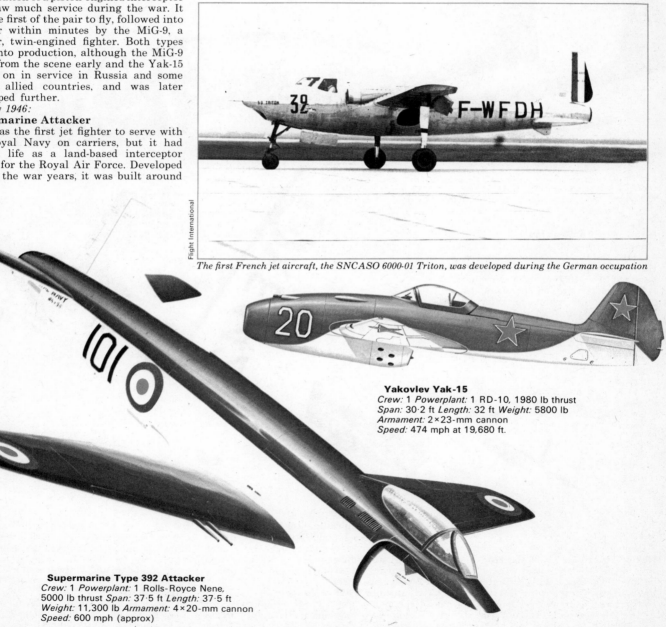

Flight International

The first French jet aircraft, the SNCASO 6000-01 Triton, was developed during the German occupation

Yakovlev Yak-15
Crew: 1 *Powerplant:* 1 RD-10, 1980 lb thrust
Span: 30·2 ft *Length:* 32 ft *Weight:* 5800 lb
Armament: 2 × 23-mm cannon
Speed: 474 mph at 19,680 ft.

Supermarine Type 392 Attacker
Crew: 1 *Powerplant:* 1 Rolls-Royce Nene,
5000 lb thrust *Span:* 37·5 ft *Length:* 37·5 ft
Weight: 11,300 lb *Armament:* 4 × 20-mm cannon
Speed: 600 mph (approx)

everything, including range – one of the more elusive performance characteristics of early, fuel-guzzling jets. That goal achieved, the Banshee stayed in the fleet to serve as a potent fighter-bomber during the Korean war some years later.

10 March 1947:
SAAB 21R
Sweden, later to become known for superlative combat aircraft, built its first jet fighter by converting a piston-engined type. This is the only known case where the same basic configuration served in both a piston-engined and jet-engined form. The SAAB J 21R could not have been a very efficient aircraft, and it was not produced in large quantity. But it served a very useful purpose, furnishing both industry and the Royal Swedish Air Force with valuable experience they could not get otherwise.

A McDonnell F2H Banshee of the US Navy, photographed in 1957 with an armament of Zuni missiles. The Banshee was virtually just a scaled up version of the earlier McDonnell Phantom

Smithsonian Institution Photo No 75-480

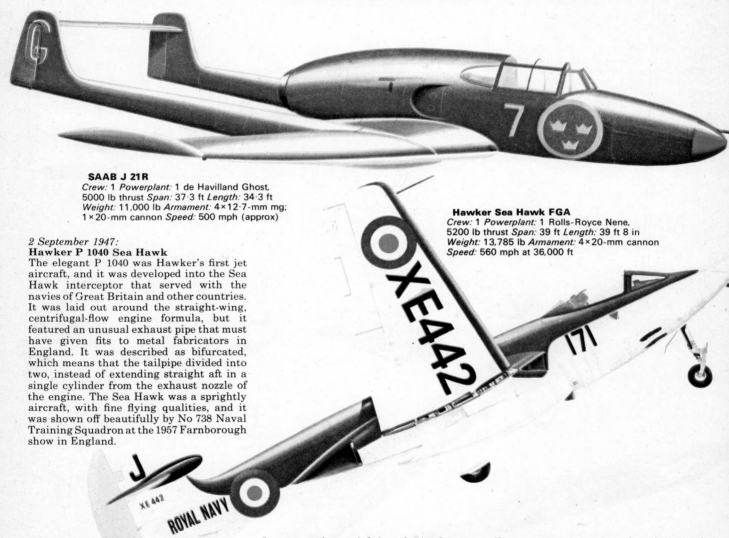

SAAB J 21R
Crew: 1 *Powerplant:* 1 de Havilland Ghost, 5000 lb thrust *Span:* 37·3 ft *Length:* 34·3 ft *Weight:* 11,000 lb *Armament:* 4×12·7-mm mg; 1×20-mm cannon *Speed:* 500 mph (approx)

Hawker Sea Hawk FGA
Crew: 1 *Powerplant:* 1 Rolls-Royce Nene, 5200 lb thrust *Span:* 39 ft *Length:* 39 ft 8 in *Weight:* 13,785 lb *Armament:* 4×20-mm cannon *Speed:* 560 mph at 36,000 ft

2 September 1947:
Hawker P 1040 Sea Hawk
The elegant P 1040 was Hawker's first jet aircraft, and it was developed into the Sea Hawk interceptor that served with the navies of Great Britain and other countries. It was laid out around the straight-wing, centrifugal-flow engine formula, but it featured an unusual exhaust pipe that must have given fits to metal fabricators in England. It was described as bifurcated, which means that the tailpipe divided into two, instead of extending straight aft in a single cylinder from the exhaust nozzle of the engine. The Sea Hawk was a sprightly aircraft, with fine flying qualities, and it was shown off beautifully by No 738 Naval Training Squadron at the 1957 Farnborough show in England.

1 October 1947:
North American XP-86 Sabre
The immortal Sabre started as a parallel design to the Fury, with a similar layout, including the straight wing. But the exciting wartime German data on swept wings led to a complete rethinking of the design concept and the alteration of the Sabre proposal to sweptwing geometry. The wings were angled back at 35°, measured at the quarter-chord line, the tail was matched to that sweep angle, and the Sabre was born.

It was an advanced fighter for its day, was built in Australia and Canada in licensed – and improved – versions, and later racked up an astonishing combat record in the high skies over MiG Alley in the Korean war.

24 November 1947:
Grumman XF9F-2 Panther
Grumman's first jet fighter followed the established and conservative formula of British jet fighters. Not that it was a bad formula to follow at that time; given the state of both engine and aerodynamic technology, the Grumman choice was as justifiable as that of North American.

Events were to prove that it was the conservative choice, but the Panther was built in quantity, maintained the Grumman reputation for fine and rugged combat aircraft, and acquitted itself well in Korea.

30 December 1947:
Mikoyan MiG-15
The thrust of an exported Nene engine from England urged this little Russian sweptwing jet fighter into the air on its first flight. Copied versions of that engine formed the basis for a later Russian industry and the powerplant for many thousands of the Red fighters. The MiG-15 became one

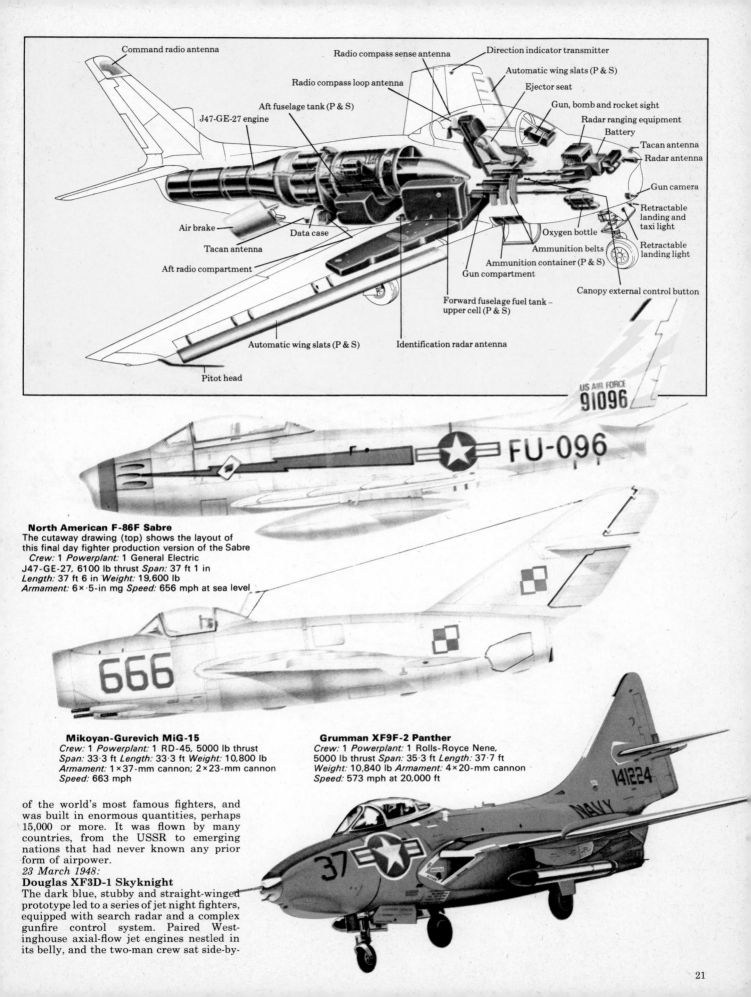

Command radio antenna

Radio compass sense antenna

Direction indicator transmitter

Radio compass loop antenna

Automatic wing slats (P & S)

Ejector seat

Aft fuselage tank (P & S)

Gun, bomb and rocket sight

J47-GE-27 engine

Radar ranging equipment

Battery

Tacan antenna

Radar antenna

Gun camera

Retractable landing and taxi light

Air brake

Data case

Retractable landing light

Tacan antenna

Oxygen bottle

Aft radio compartment

Ammunition belts

Ammunition container (P & S)

Gun compartment

Canopy external control button

Forward fuselage fuel tank – upper cell (P & S)

Automatic wing slats (P & S)

Identification radar antenna

Pitot head

US AIR FORCE 91096

FU-096

North American F-86F Sabre
The cutaway drawing (top) shows the layout of
this final day fighter production version of the Sabre
 Crew: 1 *Powerplant:* 1 General Electric
J47-GE-27, 6100 lb thrust *Span:* 37 ft 1 in
Length: 37 ft 6 in *Weight:* 19,600 lb
Armament: 6 × ·5-in mg *Speed:* 656 mph at sea level

666

Mikoyan-Gurevich MiG-15
Crew: 1 *Powerplant:* 1 RD-45, 5000 lb thrust
Span: 33·3 ft *Length:* 33·3 ft *Weight:* 10,800 lb
Armament: 1 × 37-mm cannon; 2 × 23-mm cannon
Speed: 663 mph

Grumman XF9F-2 Panther
Crew: 1 *Powerplant:* 1 Rolls-Royce Nene,
5000 lb thrust *Span:* 35·3 ft *Length:* 37·7 ft
Weight: 10,840 lb *Armament:* 4 × 20-mm cannon
Speed: 573 mph at 20,000 ft

141224

NAVY

37

of the world's most famous fighters, and
was built in enormous quantities, perhaps
15,000 or more. It was flown by many
countries, from the USSR to emerging
nations that had never known any prior
form of airpower.
23 March 1948:
Douglas XF3D-1 Skyknight
The dark blue, stubby and straight-winged
prototype led to a series of jet night fighters,
equipped with search radar and a complex
gunfire control system. Paired Westinghouse axial-flow jet engines nestled in
its belly, and the two-man crew sat side-by-

side under the cockpit canopy. Like the Sabre, Panther and MiG, the Skyknight was to go on to gain combat laurels in the Korean war.

16 August 1948:

Northrop XF-89 Scorpion

The night fighter has always been a specialised weapon, working with a combination of electronic and human sensors to seek out and destroy its prey under cover of darkness or bad weather. It needs a two-man crew to fly and to operate the complex radar, plus endurance and heavy armament. Thus it tends to be big and heavy. The Northrop XF-89 featured the same basic layout as the Skyknight, except that its crew sat in tandem positions, and it dispensed with guns as the primary

The Douglas XF3D Skyknight was a radar-equipped night fighter. Two Westinghouse engines gave it a maximum speed of 500 mph, and its armament consisted of four 20-mm cannon

Smithsonian Institution Photo No 75-4842

Northrop XF-89 Scorpion
Crew: 2 *Powerplant:* 2 Allison J35-A-15, 4000 lb thrust each *Span:* 52 ft *Length:* 50 ft *Weight:* 43,910 lb *Armament:* 6×20-mm cannon *Speed:* 608 mph

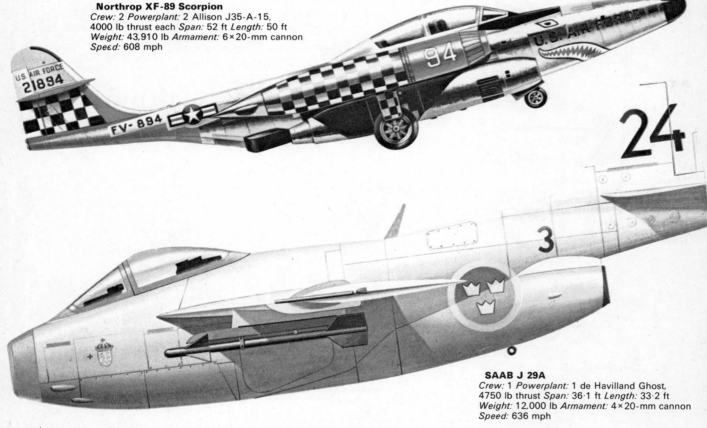

SAAB J 29A
Crew: 1 *Powerplant:* 1 de Havilland Ghost, 4750 lb thrust *Span:* 36·1 ft *Length:* 33·2 ft *Weight:* 12,000 lb *Armament:* 4×20-mm cannon *Speed:* 636 mph

weapons. It was armed with 104 small folding-fin air-to-air unguided rockets, housed in wingtip pods. They were fired in a devastating ripple pattern, rocket after rocket bursting from the pod at split-second intervals.

1 September 1948:

SAAB J 29

Europe's first sweptback wing fighter design, the barrel-shaped prototype was the first in a large quantity of the speedy Swedish fighters. Some were delivered as low-level reconnaissance aircraft, with batteries of cameras in the forward fuselage. Many years later, the J 29s served in the Congo with a United Nations force.

18 September 1948:

Convair XF-92A

The delta wing, a major technical innovation based on German experiments, first flew on the Convair XF-92A. Since there was no previous flight research experience with the new wing form, the Convair design was developed as both a flight-test aircraft and the possible prototype for an interceptor. It featured trailing-edge elevons, control surfaces that combined the functions of elevators and ailerons. Experience with the XF-92A led to Convair's later successes with the more advanced F-102A and F-106A delta-winged supersonic interceptors.

29 September 1948:

Vought XF7U-1 Cutlass

Another tailless design, but based on German sweptback wing technology rather than that of the delta shape, the Cutlass was developed for the US Navy as a carrier-based, twin-engined interceptor. Its performance was based on the use of afterburners for its jet engines, which increased the thrust substantially by adding and burning additional fuel downstream of the engine in the tailpipe. Trouble dogged the series, and the Cutlass never achieved the expected performance, what with its problematic Westinghouse jet engines and its tricky aerodynamics.

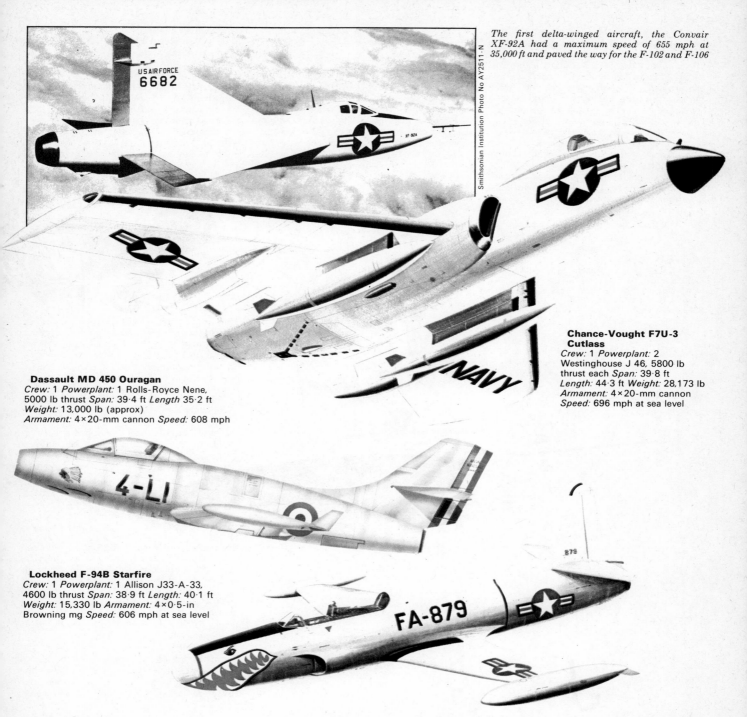

Smithsonian Institution Photo No AY2511-N

The first delta-winged aircraft, the Convair XF-92A had a maximum speed of 655 mph at 35,000 ft and paved the way for the F-102 and F-106

Chance-Vought F7U-3 Cutlass
Crew: 1 *Powerplant:* 2 Westinghouse J 46, 5800 lb thrust each *Span:* 39·8 ft *Length:* 44·3 ft *Weight:* 28,173 lb *Armament:* 4×20-mm cannon *Speed:* 696 mph at sea level

Dassault MD 450 Ouragan
Crew: 1 *Powerplant:* 1 Rolls-Royce Nene, 5000 lb thrust *Span:* 39·4 ft *Length* 35·2 ft *Weight:* 13,000 lb (approx) *Armament:* 4×20-mm cannon *Speed:* 608 mph

Lockheed F-94B Starfire
Crew: 1 *Powerplant:* 1 Allison J33-A-33, 4600 lb thrust *Span:* 38·9 ft *Length:* 40·1 ft *Weight:* 15,330 lb *Armament:* 4×0·5-in Browning mg *Speed:* 606 mph at sea level

28 December 1948:
Supermarine Type 510
This experimental prototype led directly and eventually to Britain's first sweptwing service fighter, but there were to be other prototypes with many changes before the final production configuration had been adopted. Then more than five years were to elapse between the first flight of the prototype and the early deliveries to Royal Air Force squadrons. In the end, the Swift – as the service fighter development was named – never achieved a full measure of success. It was outpaced by the advances of technology and the complexities of high-speed aircraft design.

28 February 1949:
Dassault MD 450 Ouragan
After more than two years of experimentation and trial of a variety of designs, the French produced the first in a long series of jet fighters that were to establish that country as a major exporter of aircraft. Like so many early jet designs, the Ouragan had a straight wing and a centrifugal-flow engine. But it was a major breakthrough for the French, and particularly for Marcel Dassault himself, then and still the leading exponent of private enterprise in the nationalised French aircraft industry. The Ouragan was the first French jet fighter to go into large-scale production, and was also sold abroad.

16 April 1949:
Lockheed XF-94 Starfire
The USAF sponsored continuing development of night- and all-weather fighters, hoping to counter the trend toward larger, heavier and more costly aircraft of this type. One of the successful attempts was the Starfire. Single-engined, using its afterburner for bursts of power during takeoff and at altitude, the F-94 had excellent performance for its time. Its design was an adaptation of the basic Lockheed F-80/T-33 series, so its cost was lower than it would have been if developed as a new type. Its unusual feature was the rocket armament. Like the F-89, it was also armed with folding-fin rockets, named 'Mighty Mouse' after a cartoon character of the day, and they were housed in mid-wing pods and in an annulus around the blunt nose radome.

9 May 1949:
Republic XF-91
Designed as a mixed-powerplant interceptor, the XF-91 was built around the combined thrust of a turbojet engine and a powerful four-barrelled liquid-propellant rocket engine. The theory was that the

23

rocket engine would provide super-performance at high altitudes, long after the thrust of the turbojet had fallen off to a fraction of its sea-level value. The Republic design was the first aircraft to fly with such a combined powerplant, although it was not until much later in the programme that it did so, and then not with the proposed production engine. Among the unusual technical features of the design were the inverse-taper wings, broader at the tips than at the root. This improved the low-speed performance. Additionally, the wings had variable incidence. Tandem landing gear was another innovative feature. The XF-91 was both the first and last attempt in the United States

to follow the mixed-powerplant formula, and it never progressed beyond the experimental prototype.

2 September 1949:
De Havilland DH 112 Venom
Britain's first all-weather interceptor came out of this successful fighter-bomber design. It was rather like an enlarged Vampire, with its twin tail boom layout and the egg-shaped fuselage carrying the jet engine. Its bulbous radome housed airborne intercept radar, and the two-man crew sat side by side under the broad canopy. It pioneered the use of wingtip fuel tanks in the RAF. Its wings had a modest degree of sweepback to give a straight-across trailing edge.

22 December 1949:
North American YF-95A Sabre
Originating as a modification of the Sabre line, the YF-95A (later redesignated F-86D) was designed as a night- and all-weather fighter, armed only with rockets. It required an entirely new fuselage to house a more powerful engine with an afterburner, and the nose radome changed the contours of the straight-in nose inlet of the standard Sabres. Wings, tail and landing gear came unchanged from the Sabre production line.

The single-place F-86D carried 24 Mighty Mouse rockets and had an advanced radar and gunfire control system. A simplified system and a battery of four cannon were the major changes made on the F-86K, a special version developed for export and NATO use which was produced in Italy as well as by North American.

19 January 1950:
Avro Canada CF-100
Canadian engineering developed this twin-engined, two-place all-weather fighter-interceptor with very long range to defend the extended northern borders of the country. With powerful airborne intercept radar hidden behind the nose radome, and a battery of six ·50-cal machine-guns, the CF-100 was a formidable weapon. It served in Canada and overseas with the (then) Royal Canadian Air Force, and some were exported to the Belgian air force.

3 June 1950:
Republic YF-96A Thunderstreak
This sweptwing version of the F-84 Thunderjet became a quite different aeroplane, and therefore began life under a new desig-

Republic XF-91
Crew: 1 *Powerplant:* 1 General Electric J47-GE-3 5200 lb thrust, plus 1×6000-lb thrust liquid-propellant rocket *Span:* 31·3 ft *Length:* 43·3 ft *Weight:* 28,300 lb *Speed:* 984 mph at 47,500 ft

Westland Wyvern
The Wyvern was the highest development of the torpedo strike fighter concept, but with a turbo-prop driving contra-rotating propellors it could not compete with the pure-jet naval fighter

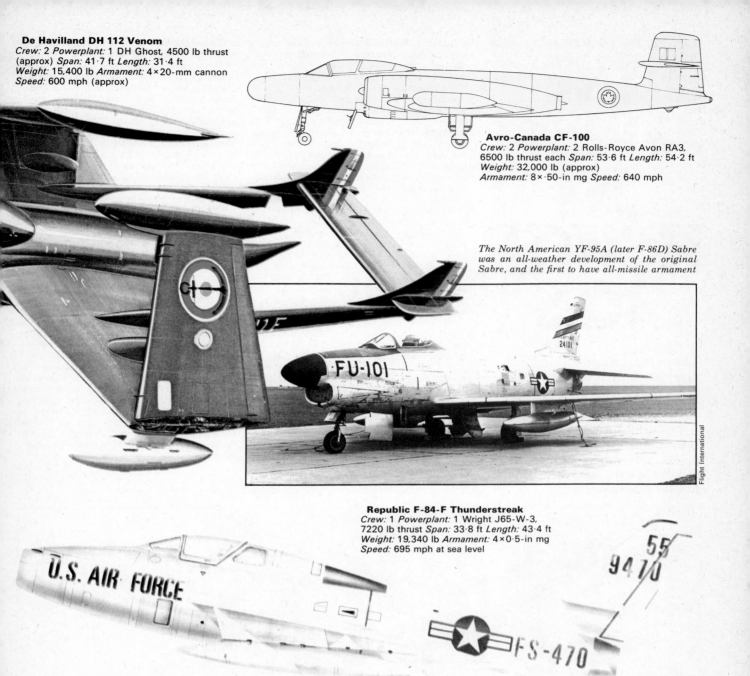

De Havilland DH 112 Venom
Crew: 2 *Powerplant:* 1 DH Ghost, 4500 lb thrust
(approx) *Span:* 41·7 ft *Length:* 31·4 ft
Weight: 15,400 lb *Armament:* 4×20-mm cannon
Speed: 600 mph (approx)

Avro-Canada CF-100
Crew: 2 *Powerplant:* 2 Rolls-Royce Avon RA3,
6500 lb thrust each *Span:* 53·6 ft *Length:* 54·2 ft
Weight: 32,000 lb (approx)
Armament: 8×·50-in mg *Speed:* 640 mph

*The North American YF-95A (later F-86D) Sabre
was an all-weather development of the original
Sabre, and the first to have all-missile armament*

Flight International

Republic F-84-F Thunderstreak
Crew: 1 *Powerplant:* 1 Wright J65-W-3,
7220 lb thrust *Span:* 33·8 ft *Length:* 43·4 ft
Weight: 19,340 lb *Armament:* 4×0·5-in mg
Speed: 695 mph at sea level

nation, later changed to F-84F. It was powered by an American-built model of a British jet engine, the Armstrong Siddeley Sapphire. But the Sapphire must have suffered in the translation, because it took an abnormally long time before the F-84F was accepted for service. This author remembers a visit to Edwards AFB during the accelerated service testing of the early production Thunderstreaks, and hearing the almost uniformly bad comments from pilots and technicians alike about the short-lived engines (as much as 25 hours between overhauls, when they were lucky) and its flying qualities (it was called the Hog, the Lead Sled, and other uncomplimentary names). But eventually the troubles were licked, and the F-84F went on to serve well in the tactical air arms of many countries as well as that of the United States.

The F-84F, like many of the aircraft developed since the end of the Second World War, was a basis for a major export programme. It happened, in almost every case, because somebody's air force wanted to convert from old-fashioned piston-engined fighters to the new jet breed, and didn't have a local industry that could develop the relatively complex airplanes. In fact, their local industry often could hardly cope with simpler types, and many a jet was to be delivered later, flown a few times until something went wrong, and left to stand on the ramp, deteriorating, unfixed and unfixable by the local talent.

The export pattern solidified early. It was clear that exporting was one way of recovering some of the high development costs of these new jet fighters and, at the same time, of exerting a powerful political and military influence on the customer country. The early postwar years saw British dominance in the marketplace with its Meteor and Vampire fighter and trainer lines. Between the two companies, they sold aircraft to 26

countries, alphabetically beginning with Argentina and ending with Venezuela. The planes were manufactured under licence in eight other countries besides Great Britain.

The United States did not, at first, sell its new jet aircraft abroad, preferring to unload some of its vast stock of piston-engined Mustangs and Thunderbolts. It was to be a while before the US industry began to take the export market very seriously.

The postwar years were characterised, then, by the maturing of wartime designs into a number of basic types of operational jet fighters. The discoveries and wild ideas of wartime were exploited in new designs and used as the foundation for further advances in technology, and the advantages of an export market became very apparent.

But the events of June 1950 were to play a very important part in the future development of jet fighters, and in the concepts of their design and operational use by opposing air forces.

25

THE FIRST JET FIGHTER ACES

The experiments with jet aircraft in the years after the Second World War, and the planes that were developed, did not have to wait long to be put to the test. In 1950 the Korean War began, and soon Russian and American Jet fighters were mixing it over war-torn Asia – not for the last time

When the North Koreans struck across their borders against South Korea early on the morning of 25 June 1950, they set in motion events that became major factors in the maturing of military jet aircraft design.

In the conflict that followed, the aerial warfare quickly became a war of interdiction, with primary roles assigned to bombers and fighter-bombers. Whatever fighter-to-fighter combat resulted was subordinate to those primary missions. This is not to downgrade the extremely valuable role of fighters in that war, but to emphasise that their missions rose out of the USAF's need to protect its bomber forces, and the North Korean and Chinese need to destroy those forces.

Some significant milestones of the jet fighter war in Korea should be recorded here. Within a week of the invasion of South Korea, USAF jets scored their first victories. Four Lockheed F-80Cs from the 35th Fighter-Bomber Squadron tangled with eight Ilyushin piston-engined attack aircraft, and shot down four of the Russian-built planes.

The first-ever combat between jet fighters was on 8 November 1950. Lt Russell J Brown, pilot of an F-80C from the USAF's 51st Fighter-Interceptor Wing, blasted a Russian-built MiG-15 that unwisely tried to out-dive the Lockheed plane.

The first victory by a North American F-86A Sabre over a MiG took place on 17 December, gained by Lt Col Bruce H Hinton. On 20 May 1951, USAF Capt James Jabara became history's first jet ace, downing his fifth and sixth MiG-15s during a single combat.

The first jet night victory was achieved by a USMC Douglas F3D-2 Skyknight, vectored by ground radar to locate a Yak-15 in the night skies over Sinui-ju.

Near the end of the war, United Nations air superiority had been established without challenge. During June 1953, USAF Sabres sighted 1268 MiG-15s, and engaged 501 of them in battle. They destroyed 77, probably destroyed another 11, and damaged 41, without losing a single Sabre all month. Those kinds of scores helped increase the highly publicised kill ratio which, near the end of the war, averaged out to better than ten to one. USAF pilots gunned down 792 MiG-15s for the loss of 78 Sabres, according to final official US figures.

What was learned? Early in the fighting, the Sabre pilots wanted more thrust – they were tired of being bounced from above by MiGs with superior altitude performance. They wanted heavier-calibre guns with a high firing rate; the ·50-cal machine-guns, so effective against German and Japanese designs during the Second World War, often failed to destroy a MiG because of the lack of striking power. And they wanted a radar-ranging gunsight, because the gyro types in the Sabres were not suitable for holding the large leads required during deflection shooting in turning combat.

Conceptually, the idea of air superiority was again tested in the skies, and the final ability of the UN air forces to fly almost anywhere without serious challenge was proof of the value, and the attainment, of that concept. Jet fighters also made good fighter-bombers, it was found, able to deliver their ordnance loads with speed and accuracy.

The end of a MiG-15, photographed with a camera mounted in the nose of an F-86 Sabre

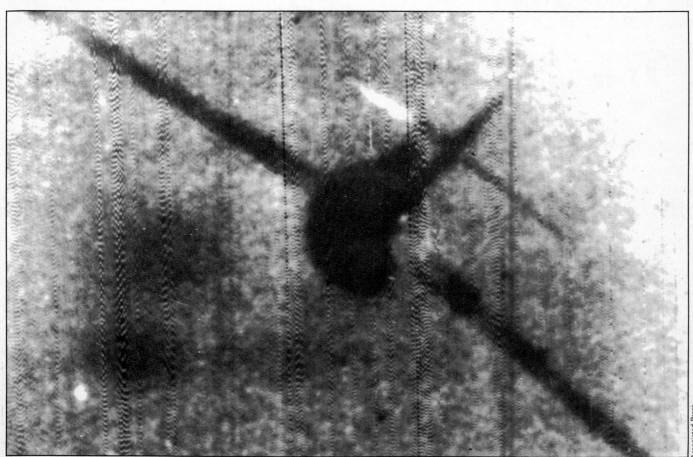

Associated Press

The idea of the long-range escort fighter grew out of early experience of the accompanied bomber raids. The B-29s operated by Strategic Air Command were slow; they were escorted by a top cover of F-86 Sabres and lower elements of Thunderjets. Typically, the attacking MiGs would streak through the top cover and go after the bombers; they were able to avoid combat with the Thunderjets by virtue of superior speed and manoeuvrability. One answer seemed to be a supersonic long-range fighter that could both escort and fight.

By the time the Korean war was seriously under way, one basic form of future air action had been further emphasised. Long-range bomber forces would continue to be one component of any future threat. The defence would be by a mix of interceptor aircraft and missiles, able to reach out with electronic senses to see, attack and destroy the bombers at either long or short range and in all kinds of weather.

This scenario, born during the Second World War, gave rise to a continuing series of fighter-interceptor designs during the decade which began with the Korean war. In the sequential descriptions that follow, note how many of the new aircraft fit into this single category.

23 January 1951:
Douglas XF4D-1 Skyray
This tailless interceptor was designed for Fleet defence under the conditions of the last months of the Second World War. It emphasised climb performance at the expense of range. Although it demonstrated its potential by setting a series of world

US jets scored heavily over MiGs in Korea, in spite of atrocious climatic conditions

Major James Jabara (with cigar), first ace of the Korean War, with two fellow pilots at their base

records, it was delayed from operational use by engine problems. Later, with those problems solved, it served well as a fighter on US carriers.

23 February 1951:
Dassault MD 452-01 Mystère
Basically a sweptwing version of the Ouragan, the Mystère prototype was the first of a series that went through extensive development, including major aerodynamic, structural and powerplant changes. It was built in quantity under off-shore procure-

ment contracts from the US, and became one of Europe's top fighter aircraft. An advanced version, the Mystère IVA, saw service in the combat in the Suez war of 1956.

20 July 1951:
Hawker P 1067
The pale green prototype was an aircraft of classic beauty. It was developed into the Hawker Hunter, first-line Royal Air Force interceptor and later ground-attack fighter. It was widely used in a variety of roles by many countries, and is regarded by many as the peak development of the subsonic jet fighter. Originating as an interceptor study built around the then-new Rolls-Royce Avon engine, it featured heavy armament and outstanding flying qualities.

7 August 1951:
McDonnell XF3H-1 Demon
The US Navy wanted this high-performance interceptor to give its carrier forces the same kind of defensive protection that land-based interceptors afforded. But the dismal failure of its Westinghouse engine to live up to requirements hamstrung the Demon from the start. It was only after long and trouble-filled delays that the type was cleared for Fleet service. The developed models served on carriers as night-fighters and as missile-armed interceptors.

20 September 1951:
Grumman F9F-6 Cougar
First sweptwing fighter in the US Navy, the Cougar was essentially a sweptwing Panther with a new horizontal tail. Development time was shortened by this fairly simple modification of the straight-winged F9F series, and the Cougars went on to serve with the Navy and the Marines as a fighter, a reconnaissance aircraft, and a trainer.

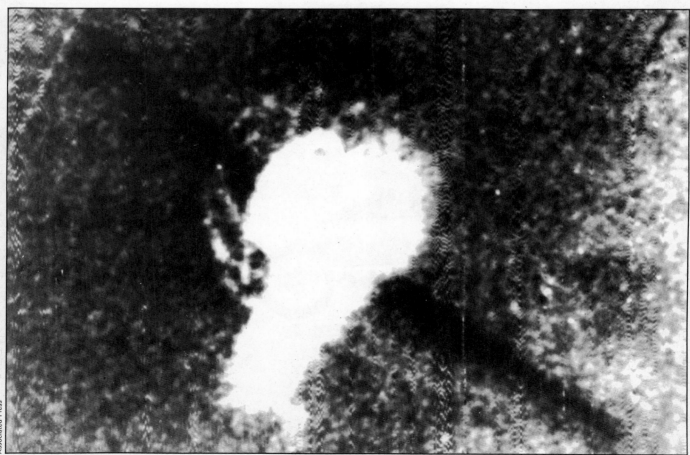

Associated Press

26 September 1951:
De Havilland DH 110
This twin-engined, two-place, twin-boomed, trans-sonic all-weather fighter was developed in response to a Royal Air Force requirement. After the structural failure and crash of the first prototype during the 1952 Farnborough show, the DH 110 was rejected in favour of the Gloster Javelin. The Royal Navy then funded the development programme and, after major redesign, the modified DH 110 was named the Sea Vixen. The first production version of that Naval all-weather interceptor flew in March 1957. It was the first British gunless interceptor, armed instead with four DH Firestreak missiles and 28 unguided rockets.

3 November 1951:
SAAB 32 Lansen
Swedish defence policy requirements for a strike fighter were the origin of this graceful and efficient two-place aircraft. Developed for a multi-role mission, the Lansen was produced as a night- and all-weather fighter in addition to its attack and reconnaissance versions. It was the first Swedish aircraft to attain supersonic speeds, flying in shallow dives to reach them for brief periods.

26 November 1951:
Gloster GA 5 Javelin
Conservatively designed as a tailed delta to improve its landing characteristics for night operations, the Javelin was the first twin-jet delta-winged aircraft to fly. It had a huge wing, in area and volume, and could

performance was to get a similar airplane. The XFJ-2, first of the Fury line, was a modified and navalised standard F-86E Sabre. Changes included arresting gear and heavier armament. But its production was slowed by increasing demands of higher priority for the F-86s, which were being built on the same production lines in the same factories. Eventually, the Fury was modified to a strike fighter with nuclear capability.

16 October 1952:
SNCASO SO 4050 Vautour
This versatile, twin-engined, two-place aircraft was produced in three versions, but

Dassault Super Mystère B-2
Last production version of the Mystère
Crew: 1 *Powerplant:* SNECMA Atar 101G, 7480 lb thrust *Span:* 34·5 ft *Length:* 46·1 ft *Weight:* 19,840 lb *Armament:* 2×30-mm cannon; 35×68-mm air-to-air rockets
Speed: Mach 1·25 at altitude

November 1952: prototype of the Hawker Hunter, probably the best subsonic jet fighter ever built

carry a large load of fuel as well as the bulky and heavy radar needed for its mission. It went through a long development period and several production versions, used both British and American radars, and lasted in service with the Royal Air Force until 1967.

27 December 1951:
North American XFJ-2 Fury
With Sabres matching and beating MiG-15 performance in Korea, the US Navy concluded that its fastest way to get similar

Above: Grumman F9F-6 Cougar, a sweptwing development of the F9F-2 Panther, and the US Navy's first sweptwing fighter. Armed with four 20-mm cannon, it had a speed of about 550 mph

Hawker Hunter 6
Crew: 1 *Powerplant:* Rolls-Royce Avon 200, 10,500 lb thrust *Span:* 33·7 ft *Length:* 45·8 ft *Weight:* 17,600 lb *Armament:* 4 Aden cannon *Speed:* 715 mph at 36,000 ft

Smithsonian Institution Photo No 75-Y841

Flight International

the greatest number were night and all-weather fighters. They were armed with a powerful battery of four 30-mm cannon and 232 air-to-air rockets in paired belly trays. This was France's only all-weather fighter for several years, and it also served that country's defences as a two-place light bomber and a single-seat strike aircraft. Some of the latter were exported to Israel, and fought with the Israeli air force in the Suez war.

2 March 1953:

SNCASO SO Trident I

Another in the periodic appearances of the super-performance manned interceptor, the Trident was a mixed-powerplant aircraft with turbojets at the wingtips and a powerful rocket motor in the fuselage. Its rate of climb was comparable to that of contemporary guided missiles, and it had high supersonic speed in level flight. Pre-production aircraft were built, but the planned production programme never materialised because of the lack of French government support.

19 May 1953:

Grumman XF10F-1 Jaguar

The date was eagerly anticipated and now is happily forgotten by senior personnel at Grumman. The Jaguar was the world's first variable-sweep aircraft and – in that respect – it performed very well, without any trouble during the entire flight-test programme. But the Jaguar was another casualty of the Westinghouse jet engine fiasco. There is one former Grumman engineering test pilot who wears a pair of Jaguar cufflinks, given by his wife to remind him that whenever things seem bad, they once were worse.

25 May 1953:

North American YF-100A Super Sabre

First of the Century Series of fighters for the USAF, the Super Sabre was designed as a tactical day fighter based on the lessons of Korea. The first approach had been to plan a new wing for the old Sabre; but a powerful new engine – the Pratt & Whitney J57 – became available, and it was decided to design around it. The combination was a winner: it was the world's first supersonic combat aircraft, and the progenitor of a long-lived line of fighters and fighter-bombers. It pioneered the low-set horizontal tail to eliminate a disastrous form of instability appearing on high-speed aircraft. Other innovations included the one-piece 'slab' horizontal tail, and the use of titanium metal for some components.

September 1953:

Mikoyan MiG-19

Opposite number to the Super Sabre, this Russian fighter became the second supersonic combat aircraft in the world. It used a twin-engined layout and contemporary aerodynamic features to develop a high-performance fighter and night-fighter that served well and long with the Soviet Union and their allied countries and friends.

24 October 1953:

Convair YF-102A Delta Dagger

Designed as an all-weather interceptor, the Delta Dagger did not, at first, meet its expected supersonic speed performance because of high drag. Happily, a development at the laboratories of the National Advisory Committee for Aeronautics (now NASA) produced a way of reducing trans-sonic drag. The YF-102 was speedily redesigned to take advantage of the 'area rule' developed by NASA's Richard T Whitcomb, and it easily slipped through the speed of sound in

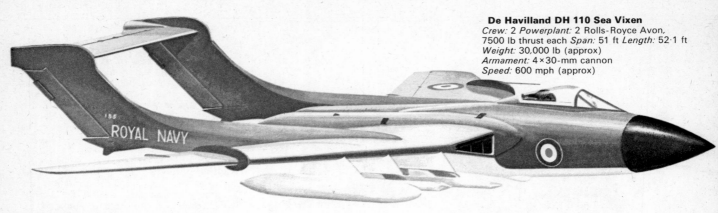

De Havilland DH 110 Sea Vixen
Crew: 2 *Powerplant:* 2 Rolls-Royce Avon,
7500 lb thrust each *Span:* 51 ft *Length:* 52·1 ft
Weight: 30,000 lb (approx)
Armament: 4×30-mm cannon
Speed: 600 mph (approx)

SAAB A32-A Lansen
Crew: 1 *Powerplant:* 1 SFA RM 5, 8050 lb thrust
Span: 42·7 ft *Length:* 48 ft *Weight:* 16,535 lb
(empty) *Armament:* 4×20-mm cannon
Speed: 700 mph at sea level

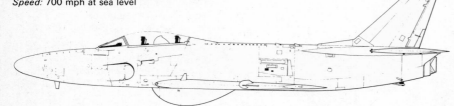

Gloster Javelin FAW 8 (foot of page)
The FAW 8 was the final production version of
the Javelin, and was equipped with American
radar equipment. Below left: Gloster Javelin
taking off
(FAW 8) Crew: 2 *Powerplant:* 2 Bristol
Siddeley Sapphire 203/204, 11,000 lb thrust each
Span: 52 ft *Length:* 56·3 ft *Weight:* 38,000 lb
Armament: 2×30-mm cannon; 4 Firestreak
missiles *Speed:* 695 mph at 10,000 ft

Flight International

Keystone
Smithsonian Institution Photo No 72-3

Above: The SNCASO SO 4050 Vautour was France's only all-weather fighter for several years, and was powerfully armed with four 30-mm cannon plus 232 68-mm unguided rockets. Above right: Engine trouble with the Grumman XF10F-1 Jaguar made it a major disappointment to its sponsors. Right: The SNCASO SO Trident was powered by two Armstrong Siddeley Vipers and a 6600-lb thrust liquid-fuel rocket. It was France's first plane capable of supersonic speeds in level flight, but in spite of its exceptionally good performance it never achieved production status

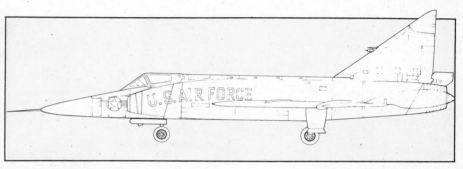

Keystone

Smithsonian Institution Photo No AY5883-D

Convair YF-102 Delta Dagger
Above, and, left, in flight
 Crew: 1 *Powerplant:* 1 Pratt & Whitney
J57-P-11, 9700 lb thrust *Span:* 37 ft
Length: 52·5 ft *Weight:* 25,000 lb (approx)
Armament: 6 Falcon guided missiles; 12×2·75-in
rockets *Speed:* 780 mph

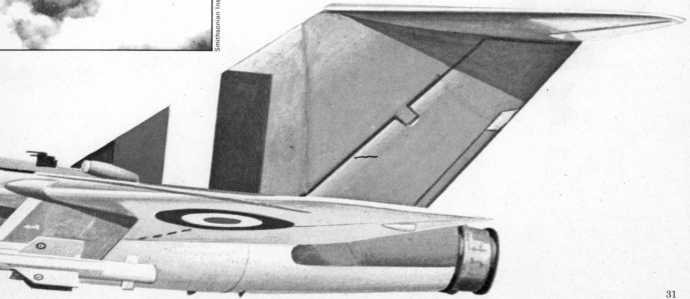

North American F-100D Super Sabre
Crew: 1 *Powerplant:* 1 Pratt & Whitney
J57-P-21A, 11,700 lb thrust *Span:* 38·8 ft
Length: 54·3 ft *Weight:* 29,762 lb
Armament: 4×20-mm cannon
Speed: 864 mph at 35,000 ft

Flight International

F-100D Super Sabres, final production version of the F-100 Sabre, at the point of takeoff

Mikoyan MiG-19
Crew: 1 *Powerplant:* 2 AM-5, 4850 lb thrust
each *Span:* 29·5 ft *Length:* 42·9 ft
Weight: 15,000 lb (approx)
Armament: 1×37-mm cannon; 2×23-mm cannon
Speed: 900 mph (approx)

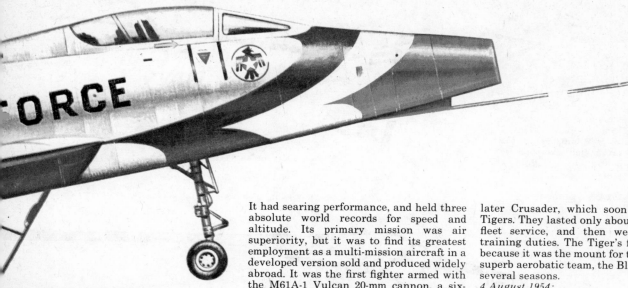

this form. The Delta Dagger was armed with Falcon guided missiles and a battery of air-to-air unguided rockets.

16 December 1953:
Dassault Mystère IVB
Just about two months after its first flight, the Mystère IVB joined the level-flight supersonic club and became the first European fighter to do so. It was one of several progressive developments of the original Mystère prototype, and used after-burning on its jet engine to improve its takeoff, climb and speed performance.

7 February 1954:
Lockheed XF-104 Starfighter
One answer to the unofficial requirements of the Korean war was the Starfighter, designed as an uncomplicated day fighter.

It had searing performance, and held three absolute world records for speed and altitude. Its primary mission was air superiority, but it was to find its greatest employment as a multi-mission aircraft in a developed version sold and produced widely abroad. It was the first fighter armed with the M61A-1 Vulcan 20-mm cannon, a six-barrelled weapon with an awesome rate of fire. It also carried Sidewinder missiles for air-to-air combat.

30 July 1954:
Grumman YF9F-9 Tiger
The area rule that benefited the Convair F-102 had been applied earlier to the Grumman YF9F-9, a major modification of the Panther/Cougar series of Naval fighters. It was later redesignated F11F-1. It preceded the area-ruled YF-102A into the air by several months, and was the first aircraft to fly with this new applied principle of aerodynamics. As one result, it became the Navy's, and the world's, first supersonic carrier-based fighter. But its delivery to the fleet was delayed by engine problems, and it began to arrive at the same time as the

later Crusader, which soon replaced the Tigers. They lasted only about two years in fleet service, and then went ashore to training duties. The Tiger's fame remains, because it was the mount for the US Navy's superb aerobatic team, the Blue Angels, for several seasons.

4 August 1954:
English Electric P 1
The angular shape of the P 1 prototype and the over-and-under arrangement of its twin engines looked like power personified. It was: the P 1 was the basis for development of the outstanding Lightning interceptor, still in active service with the Royal Air Force. It was Britain's first fighter capable of level-flight supersonic speed. Designed for the specific conditions of defence of the British Isles, the Lightning and its later

Lockheed F-104G Super Starfighter
Crew: 1 *Powerplant:* 1 General Electric J79-GE-11A, 10,350 lb thrust *Span:* 21·9 ft *Length:* 54·8 ft *Weight:* 20,900 lb *Armament:* 1 × 20-mm Vulcan cannon; 2 Sidewinder missiles *Speed:* Mach 2·2

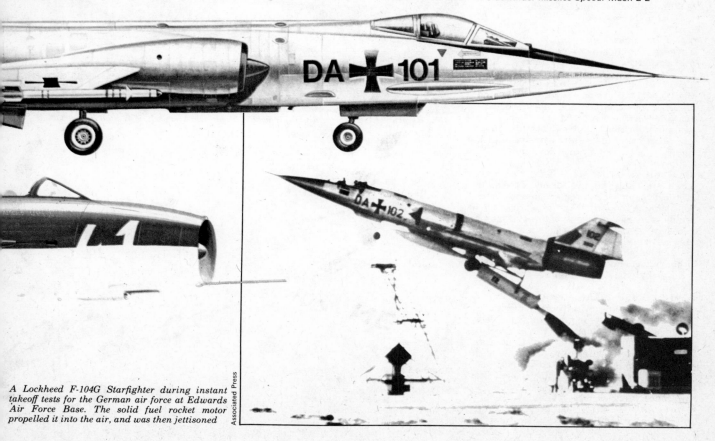

A Lockheed F-104G Starfighter during instant takeoff tests for the German air force at Edwards Air Force Base. The solid fuel rocket motor propelled it into the air, and was then jettisoned

Associated Press

33

developments were characteristically short on range but long on performance. The astounding rate of climb, coupled with automatically controlled weapons, make the Lightning a formidable fighter, even by today's high standards.

29 September 1954:

McDonnell F-101A Voodoo

USAF's Strategic Air Command, drawing on its Korean experience, wanted a long-range fighter capable of escorting bomber fleets to distant targets. The F-101 Voodoo was the result. This twin-jet, two-place

Grumman F11F-1 Tiger
Crew: 1 *Powerplant:* 1 Wright J65-W-18, 7800 lb thrust *Span:* 31·6 ft *Length:* 44·9 ft *Weight:* 21,035 lb *Armament:* 4 × 20-mm cannon; 4 Sidewinders *Speed:* 740 mph at 35,000 ft

fighter was developed from an earlier prototype, the XF-88, designed as a fighter able to strike deeply into enemy territory. SAC cancelled its requirements before the Voodoo flew, but the design was adopted by Tactical Air Command, was developed as a fighter-bomber, and later was further developed into a long-range all-weather interceptor of high performance, and a low-level photo-reconnaissance aircraft. In the latter role, Voodoos furnished many photographs of the missile sites emplaced by the Russians in Cuba in 1961.

1954:

Yakovlev Yak-25

This twin-engined, two-place night- and all-weather fighter was first seen publicly in 1955, and therefore probably flew late in 1954. As the first Russian aircraft of its type, the layout and systems were a bit behind the state of the art, a deficiency that was remedied with surprising speed in later designs from the Yakovlev design bureau. The large nose radome hints at a radar dish dimensioned for long-range detection.

2 March 1955:

Dassault Super Mystère B-2

For a quick and effective survey of the state of the French jet fighter art in the 1950s, look at the Dassault Mystère series. This model, the end of the line, was a major redesign of the basic format, featuring a thinner wing with a higher sweep angle, a redesigned windshield for lower drag, and other refinements. It easily went supersonic in level flight on its first flight.

25 March 1955:

Vought XF8U-1 Crusader

The Navy, drawing on its Korean experience, asked for a supersonic day fighter for fleet defence. The Crusader was the answer. It flew supersonically on its first flight, was the first carrier-based aircraft to exceed 1000 mph in level flight, and crossed the United States at supersonic speed. Its technical innovations included a variable-incidence wing for superb visibility during approaches to carrier landings, and full application of the area rule. Armed with

English Electric P1A, prototype Lightning, whose performance has kept it in front line service

Chance Vought F8U-2 Crusader
Crew: 1 *Powerplant:* 1 Pratt & Whitney J57-P-16, 10,700 lb *Span:* 35·2 ft *Length:* 54·5 ft *Weight:* 28,000 lb *Armament:* 4 × 20-mm cannon; 4 Sidewinders *Speed:* Mach 1·7

English Electric Lightning F1

Crew: 1 *Powerplant:* 2 Rolls-Royce Avon 200, 11,250 lb thrust each *Span:* 34·9 ft
Length: 50 ft *Weight:* 40,000 lb (approx)
Armament: 2 Aden cannon; 2 Firestreak missiles
Speed: Mach 2·1 at 40,000 ft

cannon and Sidewinder, it packed a powerful punch. At its maximum deployment, it equipped about half of the Navy and Marine fighter squadrons. It was further developed with a boundary-layer control system for the French Navy. Most recently, it fought in the Vietnam war where it acquired a reputation as the 'best gun fighter' in the theatre. It was redesignated as the F-8 Crusader in 1962.

25 June 1955:

Dassault MD 550-01 Mirage I

Like the Trident before it, the Mirage I featured a mixed powerplant. But its paired turbojets were in the fuselage, and the rocket motor was slung in a droppable package under the belly. It was the ancestor of the current Mirage III line, and was developed through a series of engine and wing changes to become France's most successful fighter, one of its best export programmes, and one of the world's best fighters, proven in combat against top-notch Russian-built aircraft in the Middle East wars.

18 July 1955:

Folland Gnat

Even though USAF pilots in Korea argued loud and long for a simple, light fighter, nobody took them seriously. All the fighters inspired by that conflict were heavier and more complex than the Sabres and MiG-15s

except for one: the Gnat. It was a small and light fighter designed to carry the optimum minimum in armament and fuel while still being an effective interceptor. The Gnat was not accepted in Britain until much later, and then only as a trainer. But Finland bought them and India built them, and they fought in the Indo-Pakistan wars, earning the nickname of 'giant-killer'.

25 October 1955:

SAAB 35 Draken

The Draken's unusual double-delta layout was SAAB's answer to a Swedish requirement for a supersonic interceptor with short takeoff and landing performance. The unusual planform was first tested on the SAAB 210, a little aeroplane with similar aerodynamics, and then translated into the full-scale Draken. Armed with cannon and missiles, the Draken has a phenomenal rate of climb and is highly manoeuvrable at low and high altitudes. It has been operated from ordinary stretches of highway, one indicator of its handling qualities and its runway requirements.

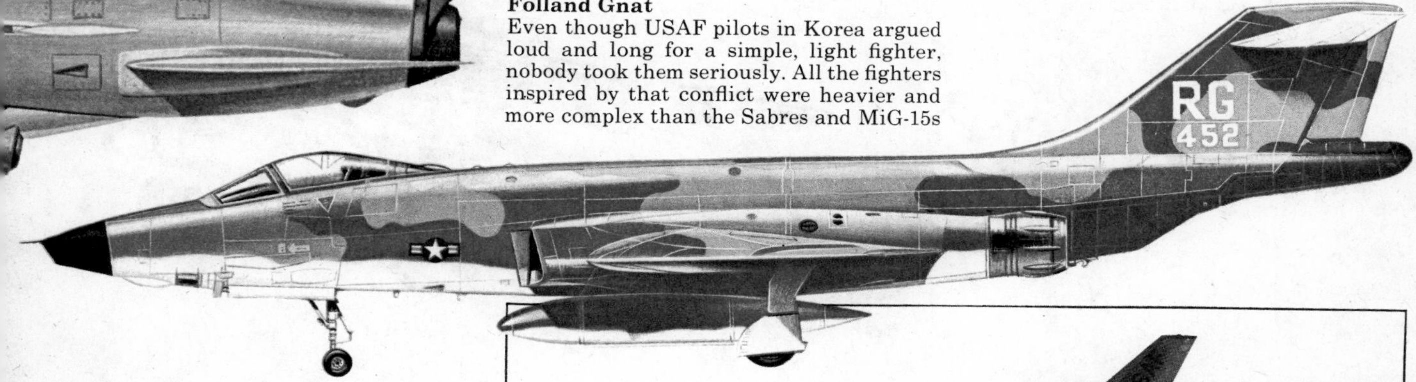

McDonnell F101A Voodoo

Crew: 1 *Powerplant:* 2 Pratt & Whitney J57-P-13 10,200 lb thrust each *Span:* 39·7 ft
Length: 67·4 ft *Weight:* 48,000 lb
Armament: 4×20-mm cannon; 3 Falcon guided missiles; 12×2·75-in unguided rockets
Speed: 1000 mph at 35,000 ft

Flight International

McDonnell F-101C Voodoos of the USAF. The F-101C is a modified and structurally strengthened version of the Voodoo for low altitude close support missions

Folland Gnat T1

Trainer version of the Gnat, shown here in the colours of the RAF Red Arrows aerobatic team
Crew: 2 *Powerplant:* 1 Bristol Siddeley Orpheus 107, 4400 lb thrust *Span:* 24 ft
Length: 37·8 ft *Weight:* 8077 lb
Armament (fighter version): 2×30-mm cannon
Speed: Mach 1·15

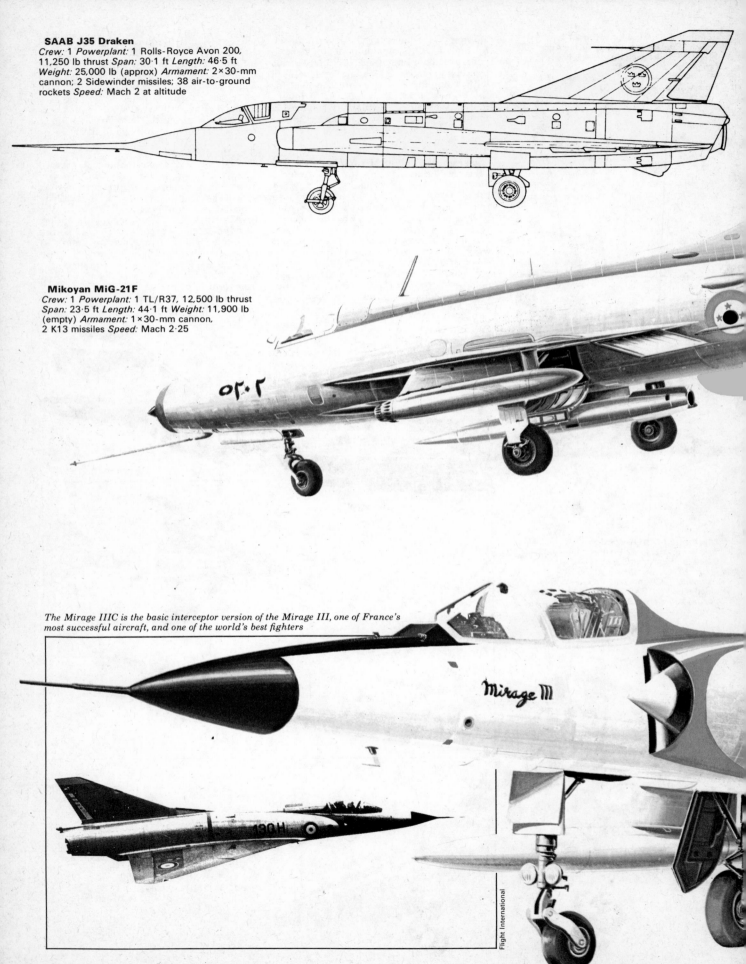

SAAB J35 Draken
Crew: 1 *Powerplant:* 1 Rolls-Royce Avon 200,
11,250 lb thrust *Span:* 30·1 ft *Length:* 46·5 ft
Weight: 25,000 lb (approx) *Armament:* 2×30-mm
cannon; 2 Sidewinder missiles; 38 air-to-ground
rockets *Speed:* Mach 2 at altitude

Mikoyan MiG-21F
Crew: 1 *Powerplant:* 1 TL/R37, 12,500 lb thrust
Span: 23·5 ft *Length:* 44·1 ft *Weight:* 11,900 lb
(empty) *Armament:* 1×30-mm cannon,
2 K13 missiles *Speed:* Mach 2·25

*The Mirage IIIC is the basic interceptor version of the Mirage III, one of France's
most successful aircraft, and one of the world's best fighters*

Flight International

1955:
Mikoyan MiG-21
First publicly seen in 1956, the MiG-21 must have made its first flight during the previous year. Primarily an all-weather interceptor with secondary ground-attack capability in some models, the MiG-21 has been widely distributed among the allies and friends of the Soviet Union. Its design is based on a thin delta with a swept horizontal tail to improve altitude performance and landing characteristics. The MiG-21 is armed with both cannon and air-to-air missiles. Its defence of North Vietnam in later years was regarded with almost universal admiration and even some envy by its adversaries.

1955:
Sukhoi Su-9
This single-engined all-weather fighter is also a tailed delta, like its contemporary, the MiG-21. But the Sukhoi design is larger, and its afterburning turbojet has a considerably higher thrust. Armament is based on missiles only, rather than on the combined cannon and air-to-air missile weaponry of the MiG-21.

20 January 1956:
Supermarine Type 544 Scimitar
This single-place sweptwing fighter for the Royal Navy was area-ruled, had power controls and blown flaps, all innovations for a Fleet Air Arm fighter. It was also the FAA's first sweptwing fighter, their first able to top supersonic speed in a shallow dive, and their first equipped to carry nuclear weapons. Its high performance was a great advance over the straight-winged Sea Hawk which it replaced in service.

23 July 1956:
Dassault Etendard
The French went to a smaller and lighter concept for their first carrier-based jet fighter. The Etendard was a loser in a NATO competition for a light fighter, but it became the basis for further development into the only true supersonic carrier-based fighter in European naval service at that time. Its design is aerodynamically similar to that of the long Mystère line, but it features layout modifications that make it more suitable for carrier use.

Smithsonian Institution Photo No 20560

The Convair F-106 Delta Dart high altitude fighter has been continuously updated, and is expected to continue in front-line service until the late 1970s

Dassault Mirage IIIC
Crew: 1 *Powerplant:* 1 SNECMA Atar 9B, 9370 lb thrust *Span:* 27 ft *Length:* 47 ft
Weight: 32,630 lb *Armament:* 2×30-mm cannon; 1 Nord AS 30 plus 2 Sidewinder missiles
Speed: Mach 2 at 36,000 ft

McDonnell F4-E Phantom
Crew: 2 *Powerplant:* 2 General Electric
J79-GE-10, 11,870 lb thrust each *Span* 38·4 ft
Length: 63 ft *Weight:* 59,000 lb (max)
Armament: 1×20-mm Vulcan cannon
Speed: Mach 2·4 at 40,000 ft

17 November 1956:
Dassault Mirage III
This was a redesigned Mirage I, and more nearly the true prototype of the contemporary line of Mirage III fighters. It used a single turbojet engine, setting the power-plant style that is maintained today in the latest of the Mirage fighters.

26 December 1956:
Convair F-106A Delta Dart
This delta-winged interceptor started life as the F-102B, but incorporated so many changes that it was redesignated with the later number. It is an automatically directed and fired weapon system; the pilot is along mostly to monitor the complex and advanced avionics systems that cram every cubic inch of this all-weather aircraft. By continuing modification programmes, this elderly design has been kept current, electronically speaking, and can handle the contemporary threat of high-altitude jet bombers. Like the F-102, it relies on both unguided and guided missiles for weapons.

16 May 1957:
Saunders-Roe SR 53
It's tempting to dismiss this as another mixed-powerplant interceptor, but its concept was a good one that ignored the ridiculous official requirements in favour of a logical design that would do the job envisioned. Unfortunately, it was caught in Britain's myopic White Paper of the late 1950s, which said that there was no fore-seeable need for a manned fighter programme beyond the English Electric P 1. That bureaucratic decision knocked out the Saunders-Roe programme as well as some other innovative British designs of the time, and set the stage for the final decline of British fighter technology.

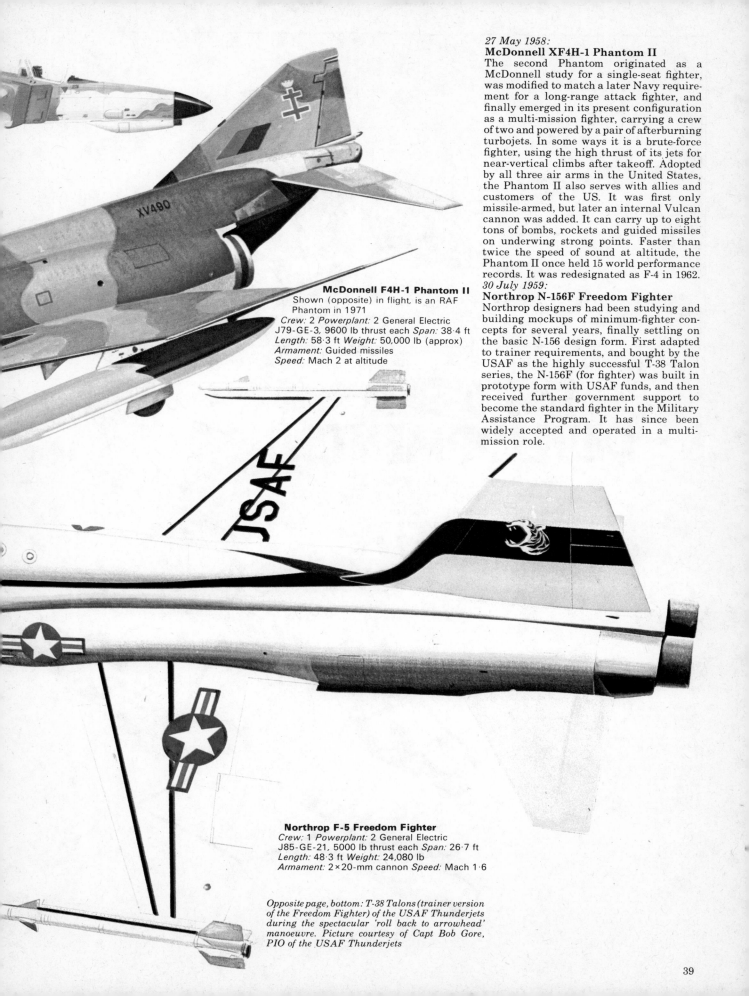

27 May 1958:

McDonnell XF4H-1 Phantom II

The second Phantom originated as a McDonnell study for a single-seat fighter, was modified to match a later Navy requirement for a long-range attack fighter, and finally emerged in its present configuration as a multi-mission fighter, carrying a crew of two and powered by a pair of afterburning turbojets. In some ways it is a brute-force fighter, using the high thrust of its jets for near-vertical climbs after takeoff. Adopted by all three air arms in the United States, the Phantom II also serves with allies and customers of the US. It was first only missile-armed, but later an internal Vulcan cannon was added. It can carry up to eight tons of bombs, rockets and guided missiles on underwing strong points. Faster than twice the speed of sound at altitude, the Phantom II once held 15 world performance records. It was redesignated as F-4 in 1962.

30 July 1959:

Northrop N-156F Freedom Fighter

Northrop designers had been studying and building mockups of minimum-fighter concepts for several years, finally settling on the basic N-156 design form. First adapted to trainer requirements, and bought by the USAF as the highly successful T-38 Talon series, the N-156F (for fighter) was built in prototype form with USAF funds, and then received further government support to become the standard fighter in the Military Assistance Program. It has since been widely accepted and operated in a multi-mission role.

McDonnell F4H-1 Phantom II
Shown (opposite) in flight, is an RAF Phantom in 1971
Crew: 2 *Powerplant:* 2 General Electric J79-GE-3, 9600 lb thrust each *Span:* 38·4 ft
Length: 58·3 ft *Weight:* 50,000 lb (approx)
Armament: Guided missiles
Speed: Mach 2 at altitude

Northrop F-5 Freedom Fighter
Crew: 1 *Powerplant:* 2 General Electric J85-GE-21, 5000 lb thrust each *Span:* 26·7 ft
Length: 48·3 ft *Weight:* 24,080 lb
Armament: 2×20-mm cannon *Speed:* Mach 1·6

Opposite page, bottom: T-38 Talons (trainer version of the Freedom Fighter) of the USAF Thunderjets during the spectacular 'roll back to arrowhead' manoeuvre. Picture courtesy of Capt Bob Gore, PIO of the USAF Thunderjets

A mid fifties revival of the parasite fighter concept, launched from the belly of an airship, teamed the giant Vultee B-36 strategic bomber with the F-84 fighter. The concept was already obsolete, and surface-to-air missiles and advanced interceptors gave the escort fighter a doubtful utility

Associated Press

DEAD END DEVELOPMENTS

During the 1940s and 1950s, boom years for jet fighter development, many strange ideas were put into practice: on these pages we illustrate some of those that were built

McDonnell XF-85
Parasite fighter of 1948, designed to be carried in the bomb-bay of a B-36 bomber. Powerplant was a Westinghouse J34 of 3400 lb thrust; span was 21 ft and length 15 ft. The unusual tail configuration was adopted for maximum flight stability

Saunders-Roe SRA-1
Saunders-Roe's postwar flying boat
development ranged from the giant Princess to
the diminuitive SRA-1 fighter, whose fuselage
incorporated a planing hull
Crew: 1 *Powerplant:* 2 Metro-Vick F2/4A
Beryl MVB1, 3850 lb thrust *Span:* 25·1 ft
Length: 45 ft *Weight:* 16,255 lb
Armament: 4×20-mm cannon *Speed:* 516 mph

The Convair XF2Y-1 Sea Dart of 1953 was the first and last hydroski jet fighter to be built. Its Westinghouse J46 engine gave it a maximum speed of 724 mph; armament was a single cannon; dimensions were 33·7 ft span and 52·6 ft length

Smithsonian Institution Photo No A Y3208-G

LESSONS FROM SMALL WARS

The wars in Vietnam and the Middle East, coupled with rapid advances in missile technology, had a profound effect on jet fighter design. Outside Russia, the emphasis switched away from pure interceptors; guns came back into fashion as armament; and the nature of local wars emphasised the usefulness of vertical takeoff aircraft

By the beginning of the 1960s, the design of jet fighters had begun to turn away from continued emphasis on interception. During the late 1950s, strategic and tactical missiles were being developed and deployed, and the nature of any offensive threat was changing. Instead of relying on a high-altitude bomber force exclusively, major powers were switching to a strike force mix of bombers and missiles. Further, bombers were being modified and crews retrained for low-level missions, to get to their targets under radar coverage and below effective anti-aircraft missile height.

This had a profound effect on fighter development. The interceptor was no longer the be-all and end-all of fighter design. There were defence planners who seriously questioned the need for any further development of manned interceptors at all. In the United States, for example, no interceptors have been designed and built since the Convair F-106A, first flown in 1956. Almost 20 years later, that aircraft is still the USAF's only all-weather interceptor.

The Russians, on the other hand, apparently still clung to the belief that the major threat against them would include strikes by manned bombers. They have continued to develop interceptors, and during the 1960s turned out five new types.

But missile strikes by major powers were considered as the ultimate recourse in some future apocalyptic event. Meantime, there were some smaller wars that had happened, that were happening, and that were about to happen. From these, too, came useful lessons for fighter designers.

The Suez crisis in 1956 clearly showed that the primary use for fighters in wars of that kind was in ground attack. They still needed residual ability to fight their way home if they were jumped by an enemy counter-air strike, but the primary job was that of airborne artillery.

Continuing aerial engagements between Israeli aircraft and adversaries from one or another of the several Arab air forces in the area taught other lessons. They re-emphasised the importance of heavy calibre cannon with high rates of fire. They redirected some

of the earlier thinking that had concentrated on missiles as the only air-to-air weapon. It became apparent that mixed armament was better than a single type of weapon, and that the ideal mix for a fighter expecting trouble was cannon and missiles, the latter being able to home on infra-red signatures or radar returns.

The vulnerability of airfields to missile strikes and to bombing – the latter point made brilliantly by the Israelis in the Six-Day War of 1967 – gave emphasis to the concept of the vertical-takeoff and vertical-landing fighter. This novel type would be able to operate from any small cleared

area – a pasture, a crossroads, a clearing in a forest – and would not be restricted to the long and very vulnerable concrete runways. It was a prototype of this new class of fighters that first flew during the first year of the time period we are considering here.
21 October 1960:

Hawker Siddeley P 1127

This prototype, built to explore the concept of vertical takeoff and landing for a tactical fighter, was developed into the first, and still the only, such fighter known to be in active service with military forces. The first flight was a captive one, made while the

P 1127 was tethered by cables to the ground. But it was the first time the aircraft left the ground under the power of its vectored-thrust turbofan engine. The P 1127 was developed further into the Kestrel and then the Harrier, a tactical fighter now in service with both the Royal Air Force and the United States Marine Corps. It is one of the truly pioneering designs in the development of fighter aircraft.
1960:

Tupolev Tu-28P

This huge, all-weather interceptor was first shown publicly in 1961, and then was lost to Western view until the 1967 display at Domodedovo, the airport near Moscow chosen for the public display that year of many new and different Russian types. The Tu-28P is a two-place, twin-engined aircraft, weighing an estimated 100,000 lb. It is very obviously capable of supersonic performance, and is armed with four air-to-air missiles externally mounted, and possibly others in an internal bay. The likelihood is that it was designed as a specific counter to high-altitude strikes by the USAF's B-58A supersonic delta-winged bomber, then in very conspicuous service with the Strategic Air Command.

Keystone

Mirage kills MiG: during the 1973 Middle East War an Israeli Mirage III downs an Arab MiG-21. Both planes first flew in the late 1950s, proved their worth during the wars of the 1960s, and continue in front line service in many parts of the world during the 1970s

1960:

Yakovlev Yak-28P

This twin-engined, two-place Russian interceptor seems at first glance to be an enlarged Yak-25. But all the indications are that it is basically a new design aerodynamically and internally, with new powerplants. It carries a pair of air-to-air missiles externally, and has trans-sonic performance. It would be capable of intercepting any subsonic bomber force targeted against Russia. The Yak-28P has been fitted with progressively updated avionics and more powerful turbojets since its service introduction.

The Hawker Siddeley Harrier provides a complete contrast to the YF-12 concept. A subsonic V/STOL aircraft, it is designed specifically to meet the conditions encountered in local wars

Hawker Siddeley Aviation

The Lockheed YF-12A long-range interceptor, capable of sustained flight at Mach 3+ at altitudes of over 80,000 ft, was the peak development of supersonic cruise aircraft in the early 1960s. It was largely redundant as a fighter, however, and became the SR-71 strategic reconnaissance aircraft

Smithsonian Institution Photo No 20560

26 April 1962:
Lockheed YF-12A

There have been USAF requirements for advanced manned interceptors from time to time, and the development of the YF-12A may have resulted from one of them. Or it might have been simply a cover operation to conceal the development of the SR-71 strategic reconnaissance aircraft. In either case, the dark blue-black YF-12A prototypes were built as potential interceptors, optimised for cruise speeds three times that of sound at altitudes above 80,000 ft. They carried missiles in belly bays. The unusual

layout, with its lifting-body aerodynamics and canted twin tails, represented the peak of the development of supersonic cruise design features at that time. The configuration was later modified slightly to produce the unarmed SR-71, a global reconnaissance aircraft that collects data supplementing that obtained from satellite photography.

21 December 1964:
General Dynamics F-111

Variable-sweep wings had been tried and studied, with varying degrees of success, for nearly twenty years when a technical

innovation developed by the US National Aeronautics and Space Administration offered promise for a practical application. The idea was to pivot the wing sections outboard, rather than on the aircraft centreline. Technically, it worked. Then USAF and Navy fighter requirements and a new Secretary of Defence combined with the NASA innovation to give birth to the TFX, a multi-role combat aircraft that was intended to become the standard tactical fighter with all three US air arms. In the event, only the USAF got the developed TFX, or the F-111, as it was later designated after four design competitions and evaluations, and a controversial production contract. But the performance of the variable-sweep plane has marked it as one of the outstanding fighter designs of any era, and assured it of a place in aeronautical history. Missile-armed and loaded with advanced avionics, the F-111 series serves with Tactical Air Command and the Australian air force. In its FB-111A version, it equips two Strategic Air Command medium-bomber wings.

1964:
Sukhoi Su-11

On display at Domodedovo in 1967, the Su-11 attracted notice as an obvious further development of the same designer's Su-9, then in widespread service as an all-weather fighter with the Red air forces. The Su-11 follows the same formula of the single-engined, single-seat all-weather fighter, but it carries improved missiles under its delta wings, has a longer fuselage nose, and an engine with perhaps a 20% thrust increase. It is supersonic, reaching speeds close to Mach 2 at altitude.

1964:
Sukhoi Su-15

Second of the new Sukhoi designs to be shown in 1967 at the Domodedovo display, the Su-15 all-weather fighter forsakes the single-engine scheme for the power of twin turbojets with afterburning for super performance. Its aerodynamic layout draws heavily on the design bureau's experience with the Su-9 and Su-11, but the basic wing has been modified in one prototype to produce a compound-sweep planform. Another version of the Su-15, modified for short takeoff and landing operations, was also displayed and flown at Domodedovo.

1964:
Mikoyan MiG-23

The Russian application of variable-sweep geometry to a fighter produced the MiG-23, a smaller and lighter aircraft than the F-111 series, although designed for approximately the same missions. It is a single-seat, single-engined tactical fighter and fighter-bomber, armed with a twin-barrelled 23-mm cannon. Performance estimates place it in the Mach 2 class at altitude. Apparently the MiG-23 ran into some development troubles, because it was not until several years after the first public display at Domodedovo in 1967 that it was reported in active service with front-line squadrons. It has since been exported to Russian allies and friends, including those in the Middle East arena.

1964:
Mikoyan MiG-25

An all-weather interceptor with phenomenal performance, the MiG-25 has been the standard of comparison and of the fighter threat in almost any consideration of strategic or tactical aircraft design in the West during the past decade. The speedy

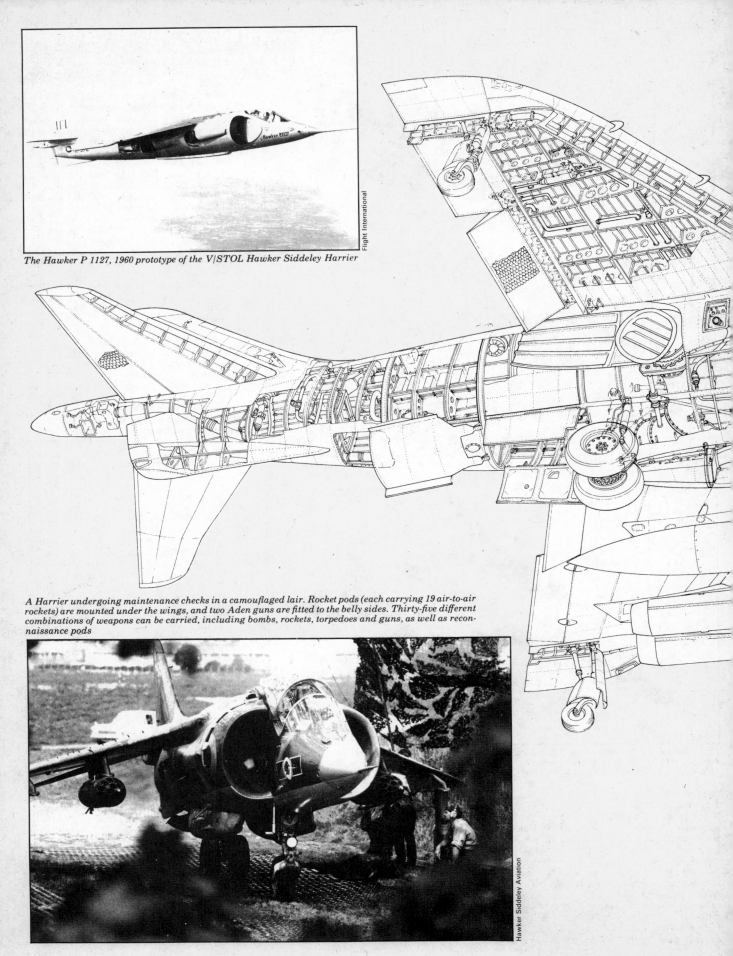

Flight International

The Hawker P 1127, 1960 prototype of the V/STOL Hawker Siddeley Harrier

A Harrier undergoing maintenance checks in a camouflaged lair. Rocket pods (each carrying 19 air-to-air rockets) are mounted under the wings, and two Aden guns are fitted to the belly sides. Thirty-five different combinations of weapons can be carried, including bombs, rockets, torpedoes and guns, as well as reconnaissance pods

Hawker Siddeley Aviation

THE HARRIER

The Hawker Siddeley Harrier V/STOL is unique among serving combat aircraft. The prototype P 1127 first flew in 1960; the Harrier itself in August 1966. At present serving with the RAF and US Marine Corps, the Sea Harrier version will shortly enter service with the Royal Navy.
Crew: 1 *Powerplant:* 1 Rolls-Royce Pegasus 11, 21,500 lb vectored thrust *Span:* 25·3 ft *Length:* 45·5 ft *Speed:* 680 mph at sea level

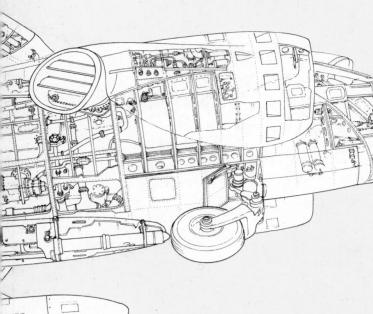

The Harrier can lift one-third of its maximum load in vertical takeoff (below). In a short takeoff run (approximately a quarter of that required by conventional combat aircraft) it can lift a fuel and weapons load of 13,050 lb – greater than its own empty weight of 12,200 lb

Pilot Press

Yakovlev Yak-28P
Crew: 2 *Powerplant:* 2 RD11, 13,100 lb thrust
each *Span:* 42·5 ft *Length:* 71 ft
Weight: 30,000 lb (approx)
Armament: 2 air-to-air missiles
Speed: 730 mph (approx) at altitude

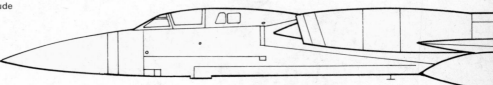

Tupolev Tu-28P
Crew: 1 *Powerplant:* 2 afterburning jets,
27,000 lb thrust each (estimate) *Span:* 65 ft
Length: 85 ft *Weight:* 100,000 lb
Armament: 4 air-to-air guided missiles
Speed: Mach 1·75 at altitude

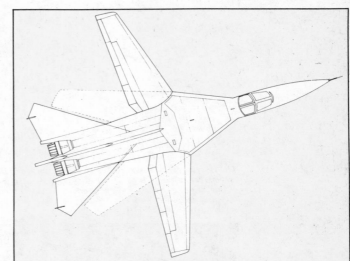

Mikoyan MiG-23
Crew: 1 *Powerplant:* 1 afterburning turbojet,
9300 lb thrust (estimate) *Span:* 46·7 ft
Length: 55·1 ft *Weight:* 12,700 lb
Armament: 2×23-mm cannon
Speed: Mach 2·3 at altitude

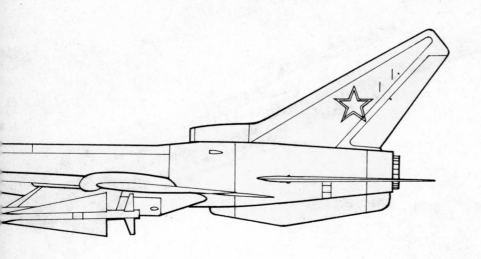

twin-jet design held several absolute world speed and time-to-climb records, and held some of them unbeaten for nearly ten years. (In early 1975, the time-to-climb records, the last of the batch held by the MiG-25, were topped, and substantially, by a USAF McDonnell F-15A Eagle.) It carries four air-to-air missiles of a new type beneath its stubby swept wings, and can do better than Mach 3 at altitude. In a reconnaissance version, the MiG-25 has been observed, but not intercepted, in high-level flights in the Middle East. It is a single-place aircraft.

23 December 1966:

Dassault Mirage F 1

Like so many of the series of advanced Dassault designs, this one grew out of earlier attempts to meet an entirely different requirement. The F 1 was developed into a multi-mission fighter, with its greatest strength in the air-superiority role. Yet its genesis was as a flying test bed aircraft built for development work with a new engine planned for a Dassault VTOL fighter. It is a single-seat fighter, powered by a single SNECMA Atar engine, probably the final development of that long line that traces its ancestry all the way back to the Junkers 004B. The F 1 wing design uses advanced aerodynamic features, tried and tested on other Dassault aircraft and refined for optimum performance in the specific F 1 configuration. Rugged landing gear gives the F 1 the ability to operate out of grass strips, or from unimproved airfields. It carries very heavy armament; as an interceptor, for example, it is armed with a pair of 30-mm cannon, a pair of Matra R 530 radar-homing missiles, and another pair of air-to-air missiles at the wingtips. It has been ordered by the French air force and will undoubtedly be sold abroad as well.

8 February 1967:

SAAB System 37 Wiggen

The Wiggen is the major component of a complete air defence system, and the product of a most ambitious effort by Sweden that can stand comparison to any such effort by any country. The Wiggen aircraft was designed to be a flying platform capable of carrying a variety of sub-systems into the air for a variety of missions. Four major missions were chosen for the development: strike, reconnaissance, interception, and training. These requirements were all built into the airplane as far as possible, so that the final result is a multi-mission aircraft with cross-capabilities. Its unique aerodynamic layout with its main wing and the forward, separate, auxiliary wing produces low approach speeds. With thrust reversers, the Wiggen can land in less than 1700 ft of runway. Its low-speed characteristics give it STOL (short takeoff and landing) performance and it can operate from highways. At altitude it can streak along at twice the speed of sound. It carries missiles and advanced avionics for navigation and attack.

The SAAB Wiggen, Dassault F 1 and General Dynamics F-111, all multi-mission fighters, are one product of their times. Capable of a wide range of performance, from STOL to supersonic, and able to arm with missiles for dog-fighting or bombs for ground attack, their versatility assures them of continued use in the air arms of their respective countries.

But they begin to show a trend which will be accentuated in the next time period by the Grumman F-14A and the McDonnell F-15A. That trend will force another look at the philosophy of fighter design.

Flight International

The variable-sweep F-111 was dogged by trouble during its development

General Dynamics F-111A
Above left (in box): diagram of F-111 variable-sweep wing configuration
Crew: 2 *Powerplant:* 2 Pratt & Whitney TF30-P-1, 18,500 lb thrust each (with afterburning) *Span:* 63 ft (spread) 32 ft (swept) *Length:* 73·5 ft *Weight:* 92,657 lb
Armament: 1 × 20-mm Vulcan cannon; air-to-air missiles *Speed:* 1450 mph at 40,000 ft

The SAAB J37 Wiggen, another competitor in the race to replace Europe's combat aircraft

Flight International

Keystone

Marcel Dassault, designer and builder of the Mystère/Mirage series, started his career in aviation during the First World War

Flight International

Dassault Mirage F1, the French candidate to replace the obsolescent NATO Starfighters

Dassault Mirage F1
Crew: 1 *Powerplant:* 1 SNECMA Atar 09K-50,
11,023 lb thrust *Span:* 27·5 ft *Length:* 49·3 ft
Weight: 24,000 lb *Armament:* 2×30-mm cannon;
2 Sidewinders plus other missiles
Speed: Mach 2·2 at altitude

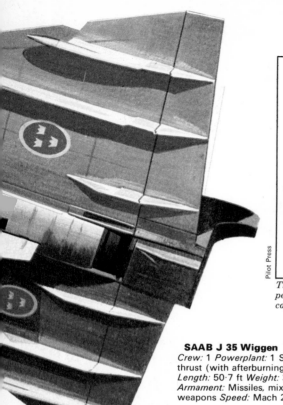

Pilot Press

The Mikoyan MiG-25 set the standard of jet fighter performance for a decade, and its phenomenal performance was only recently bettered by the F-15 Eagle. It carries four air-to-air missiles, and is capable of Mach 3·2 at altitude

SAAB J 35 Wiggen
Crew: 1 *Powerplant:* 1 Svenska RM8, 26,500 lb thrust (with afterburning) *Span:* 34·8 ft
Length: 50·7 ft *Weight:* 35,000 lb (approx)
Armament: Missiles, mixed external stores and weapons *Speed:* Mach 2 at high altitude

Flight International

The Dassault Mirage G 8 swing-wing fighter, from which Dassault are developing the Super Mirage fighter

Keystone

SOARING COST AND COMPLEXITY

The escalating costs of fighters like the Grumman Tomcat are causing much heart-searching among aircraft firms and Defence Ministries, and it begins to seem that the General Dynamics YF-16 is the fighter concept of the future

The aerial war in Vietnam continued to teach the same truths about fighter design. Versatility was one such lesson. A fighter-bomber might have to carry bombs on one sortie, rockets on the next, napalm on its third and guns on its fourth. Or it might have to take off with a mixture of all these and, after dumping them, fight its way back home through a curtain of intense flak and enemy missiles.

The concept of a multi-mission fighter was reinforced by Vietnam experience. It also added new emphasis to a lesson from earlier wars: the importance of electronic countermeasures. Electronic warfare had come to the battlefields of Southeast Asia with a vengeance; their environment was criss-crossed with invisible beams of electronic devices for finding, fooling and helping to destroy aircraft.

A major impetus to the growth of electronic warfare was the advance of the guided missile as an anti-aircraft weapon. It could not be shot down; it had to be evaded or avoided or decoyed some way. Evasion techniques had been developed, but – as missile technology improved – the dependence on spotting and manoeuvring grew riskier. The next stop: decoy the missile by giving it a false target to detect, track and intercept. This could be done electronically or physically.

Electronic warfare systems added to fighter capabilities. They could warn a pilot that his plane had been detected; that it was under fire from the rear; and that the missile was beginning its final tracking toward a hit on his plane. These passive indications could be augmented by electronic countermeasures activity. They could, in effect, create a cloud of electronic noise in which the fighter might hide. They could create a completely spurious fighter that would have a stronger attraction for the oncoming missile. They could confuse the missile, decoy it, send it to another quadrant of the sky.

Brains, even electronic ones, are not built cheaply. Further, like human brains, they function best in friendly environments; they tend to be troubled by excessive heat, cold, or physical shocks. Making electronic brains that can withstand those deteriorating factors and still perform involves more complexity, and that equates to more cost.

The US Navy's best and most expensive fighter, the swing-wing Grumman F-14A Tomcat undergoing flight tests over San Clemente Island

And so, as each side added an offensive technique or countered one with a defensive technology, the inevitable happened. Fighters got more complex, and consequently more costly to build.

When the Vietnam aerial action really began in the early 1960s, a North American F-100, then a standard day fighter, could be bought for about $600,000 flyaway factory. If one wanted the greater capability of a McDonnell F-4C, the price was tripled to $1·8 million.

These kinds of cost figures were impressive, especially to those who remembered 1958, when it was possible to get a North American F-86F, then the top-of-the-line day fighter, for $230,000.

But the price of an F-4C was only an indication of the trend. The data were coming in on the then-new General Dynamics F-111 series, with costs – according to testimony in the bitter but fascinating Congressional hearings – of more than $16 million per airplane. Admittedly this was a special case, but it served to send up warning flags. In the depths of the Pentagon in Washington, DC, fighter analysts and planners began to look for alternatives to the high-cost development and production of today's fighters.

Costs and contracts

The final straw, perhaps, was the sobering experience shared by the Navy and Grumman in the development of the variable-sweep F-14A Tomcat series. Cost escalations, caused by inflationary factors and other problems, threatened the continued existence of Grumman as a company. The Navy wanted to hold Grumman to the fixed prices guaranteed in its contract; Grumman said that doing that would bankrupt the company, and claimed that the rules under which the contract had been written had made assumptions that were no longer valid. It was unfair to hold Grumman to those rules, they said.

After some recriminations and refinancings, the programme continued and the Tomcat entered the fleet, where it is serving with great distinction. It is costing the US Navy, and the American taxpayer, about $11 million per airplane, based on a system of accounting which produces agreement between Navy and Air Force cost figures.

The McDonnell-Douglas F-15A Eagle, a fighter, costs about 10% less than the variable-sweep Tomcat.

These amounts of dollars, it might be noted, could have bought a complete Boeing B-52 towards the end of that bomber's production life in 1962, at about the time that the top fighter, the F-4, was purchased for less than $2 million.

It should be realised that costs for aircraft may or may not include all the programme costs amortised out over each airplane. At one end of the cost scale is simply the amount of money the military

pays to the manufacturer for building and assembling the parts that make up one complete airplane. At the other end is the total cost of research, development, tooling, flight test, problem-solving, and all the rest of the programme, including production, for each plane.

The figure of $16·6 million, quoted in Congressional testimony for the F-111, is the total programme cost divided by the number of airplanes produced. In the Grumman F-14A and McDonnell-Douglas F-15A figures cited above, the programme costs are not all included in the airplane's price. To do so might double the figures.

There is black humour used by proponents of low-cost aircraft to make a point. They plot the cost of a fighter (or bomber or whatever) against time, and show how that curve has climbed upward more and more rapidly until, at some date not very far away, the cost of a single fighter exceeds the total US budget. They then speak of the Air Force as flying its fighter, or its bomber, against an enemy strike.

The use of such a simplistic approach dramatises the central fact: fighter costs are escalating out of sight. And a major portion of that cost is chargeable to inflation. By mid-1974, inflation in the price of metals that go into aircraft construction had accounted for more than a 60% rise in materials costs since 1967, or more than 8% annually.

Even stronger was the impact of worldwide inflation during the last few months of 1973. A Department of Defense estimate attributed a 36% cost rise in more than 50 major weapons systems to the financial near-panic of that period.

In some ways, the cost growth of fighter aircraft has been a result of evolution, rather than revolution, in design. It is common to base a new fighter on the latest successful one operational, because the fastest and lowest-cost way has been thought to be by that route. What this meant in practice is that the latest technology, which might have been able to reduce costs if effectively applied, was not used. An existing design was adapted and, although it often brought an apparent low cost with it because of its status as a high-production, amortised programme, it could wind up costing more because of fix after fix necessary to bring the ageing design up to date.

In the early 1970s, the USAF funded a development programme that aimed at reversing the trend to higher costs. The purpose was to evaluate the latest in fighter technology in minimum-sized aircraft, with the primary goal of seeing what could be done with new technology when a preconceived military mission was not a factor in design.

The General Dynamics YF-16 and Northrop YF-17 were the interesting results of that programme. Two different airplanes, they reflect their company's approaches to the design of a lightweight fighter type of aircraft, with carte blanche to use any new idea as long as it appeared promising.

Both these refined designs have won high marks from observers for their adherence to requirements and their low-cost approach.

In early 1975, prices for both were estimated at about $4 million each, should a large-scale production programme follow. This is still an expensive fighter, but it is a remarkable achievement to reach cost figures about one-third those of the immediate predecessors.

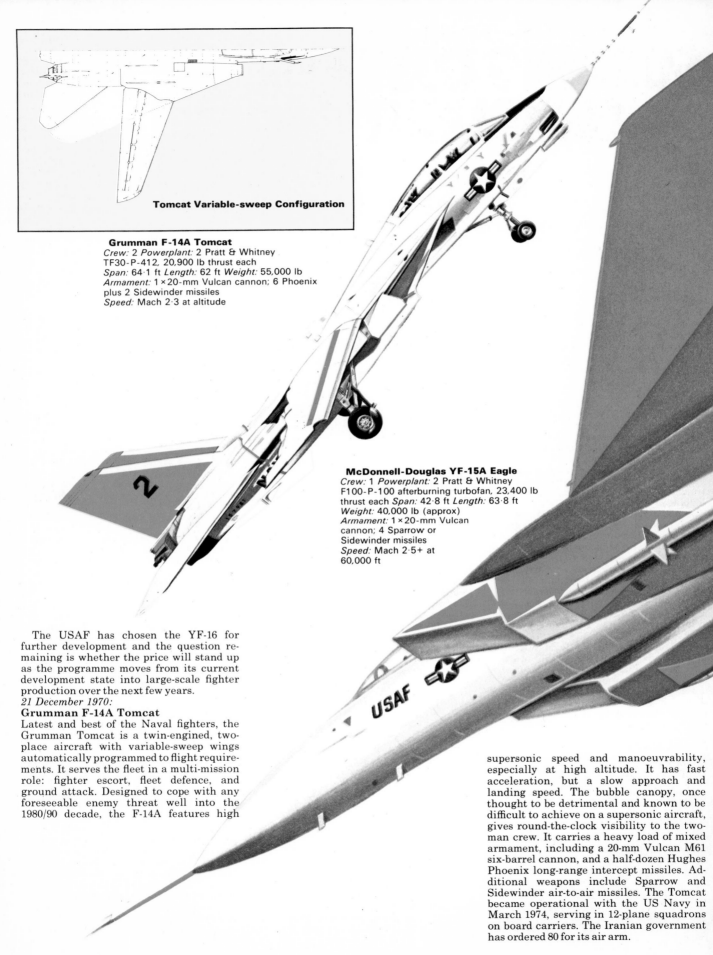

Tomcat Variable-sweep Configuration

Grumman F-14A Tomcat
Crew: 2 *Powerplant:* 2 Pratt & Whitney
TF30-P-412, 20,900 lb thrust each
Span: 64·1 ft *Length:* 62 ft *Weight:* 55,000 lb
Armament: 1×20-mm Vulcan cannon; 6 Phoenix
plus 2 Sidewinder missiles
Speed: Mach 2·3 at altitude

McDonnell-Douglas YF-15A Eagle
Crew: 1 *Powerplant:* 2 Pratt & Whitney
F100-P-100 afterburning turbofan, 23,400 lb
thrust each *Span:* 42·8 ft *Length:* 63·8 ft
Weight: 40,000 lb (approx)
Armament: 1×20-mm Vulcan
cannon; 4 Sparrow or
Sidewinder missiles
Speed: Mach 2·5+ at
60,000 ft

The USAF has chosen the YF-16 for further development and the question remaining is whether the price will stand up as the programme moves from its current development state into large-scale fighter production over the next few years.
21 December 1970:
Grumman F-14A Tomcat
Latest and best of the Naval fighters, the Grumman Tomcat is a twin-engined, two-place aircraft with variable-sweep wings automatically programmed to flight requirements. It serves the fleet in a multi-mission role: fighter escort, fleet defence, and ground attack. Designed to cope with any foreseeable enemy threat well into the 1980/90 decade, the F-14A features high supersonic speed and manoeuvrability, especially at high altitude. It has fast acceleration, but a slow approach and landing speed. The bubble canopy, once thought to be detrimental and known to be difficult to achieve on a supersonic aircraft, gives round-the-clock visibility to the two-man crew. It carries a heavy load of mixed armament, including a 20-mm Vulcan M61 six-barrel cannon, and a half-dozen Hughes Phoenix long-range intercept missiles. Additional weapons include Sparrow and Sidewinder air-to-air missiles. The Tomcat became operational with the US Navy in March 1974, serving in 12-plane squadrons on board carriers. The Iranian government has ordered 80 for its air arm.

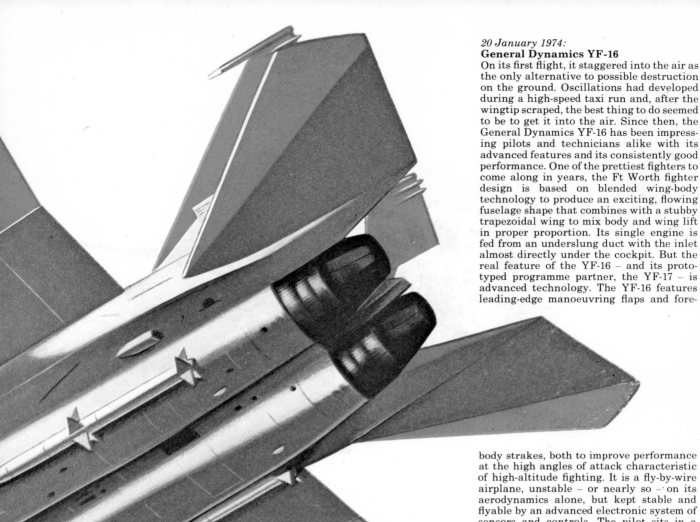

20 January 1974:
General Dynamics YF-16

On its first flight, it staggered into the air as the only alternative to possible destruction on the ground. Oscillations had developed during a high-speed taxi run and, after the wingtip scraped, the best thing to do seemed to be to get it into the air. Since then, the General Dynamics YF-16 has been impressing pilots and technicians alike with its advanced features and its consistently good performance. One of the prettiest fighters to come along in years, the Ft Worth fighter design is based on blended wing-body technology to produce an exciting, flowing fuselage shape that combines with a stubby trapezoidal wing to mix body and wing lift in proper proportion. Its single engine is fed from an underslung duct with the inlet almost directly under the cockpit. But the real feature of the YF-16 – and its proto-typed programme partner, the YF-17 – is advanced technology. The YF-16 features leading-edge manoeuvring flaps and fore-body strakes, both to improve performance at the high angles of attack characteristic of high-altitude fighting. It is a fly-by-wire airplane, unstable – or nearly so – on its aerodynamics alone, but kept stable and flyable by an advanced electronic system of sensors and controls. The pilot sits in a reclining position for a higher level of tolerance to accelerations of combat turns, and flies the YF-16, not with a central control stick, but with a side-arm controller mounted at the right of the cockpit. Armed with a single Vulcan cannon and a pair of Sidewinder dog-fighting missiles, the YF-16 also can carry external stores and weapon pods on seven underwing strong points.

9 June 1974:
Northrop YF-17

The other half of the lightweight fighter programme flew about six months later, and revealed a different approach from the one chosen by General Dynamics. The YF-17 designers used a pair of smaller engines, citing the dependability and reliability of a twin-engined installation, verified in practice with their F-5/T-38 line. Aerodynamically, the YF-17 builds on advanced technology, using a refinement of the basic Tiger II wing and a forward modification of that surface. A shoulder-wing design, the Northrop fighter uses twin canted vertical tails. Engine intakes are what have been inelegantly called armpit types, located between wing root and the fuselage side. Armament is identical to that of the YF-16. Northrop designers optimised their aircraft around the turning rate performance, which they had concluded was the single most important factor in aerial combat. The radius of turn, the ability to pull high loads during the turn, and all the other arguments of pilots and technicians were boiled down to a shape and a powerplant that would get the nose of the airplane turned into a fight as rapidly as possible.

27 July 1972:
McDonnell-Douglas F-15A Eagle

For the first time in a quarter of a century, the USAF has a fighter optimised specifically for the air-superiority mission. The single-seat Eagle is built around a stubby sweptwing of low aspect ratio and high area, for extra manoeuvrability at high altitude. It carries mixed armament: a 20-mm Vulcan cannon, and Sidewinder and Sparrow missiles, updated specifically for dog-fighting at closer ranges. Early in 1975, the Eagle set eight world time-to-altitude records in flights under the project name of Streak Eagle. In timed climbs from three to 30 kilometres, the Eagle broke mark after mark in a staggering performance with numbers that almost defy the imagination. On the climb to three kilometres, the F-15A lifted off the ground after a roll of 400 ft, about seven lengths of the fuselage. On a single flight which broke three of the existing records, the F-15A accelerated to sonic speed within 19 seconds after takeoff. In the climb to the highest altitude, the pilot accelerated in climb to Mach 2 in less than two minutes from takeoff, and the subsequent energy climb got him to 102,000 ft before the Eagle slacked off. In less than one minute, the Eagle reached 12 kilometres (39,360 ft); its average rate of climb to 30 kilometres (98,400 ft) was better than 144 metres per second, or 28,438 ft per minute.

The rapid increases in cost and complexity are not the only considerations in assessing the future of the jet fighter. Most fighters of the last 20 years have had some capacity as strike/attack/reconnaissance aircraft, while some high performance interceptors such as the YF-12 and F-111 have failed to get into service. History is not encouraging, and the future is far from clear

Are the YF-16 and YF-17 the trend-setters for future fighter design? Or are they slated to be remembered as brilliant design efforts that gradually turned into heavy, complex and costly multi-purpose fighters?

History does not provide much encouragement for answering the first question positively. The one recent example – the Folland Gnat – was a successful approach to the problem, and it offered some unique and innovative solutions, but alone it could not stem the tide.

The avowed purpose of the YF-16/YF-17 programme was to develop a fighter-type aircraft without the need to meet a specific operational requirement for one. For that reason, the design teams at General Dynamics and Northrop were free to apply any late technology, almost without regard for its suitability in a combat aircraft.

But neither company got where it is by

THE FUTURE

WHERE DO WE GO FROM HERE?

being unaware of military requirements. Consequently, both aircraft reflect the extensive experience of their manufacturers in the development of recent high-speed combat aircraft. Further, along the line the Air Force began to have second thoughts about the programme, and let it be known that they might consider developing the better of the two into a combat-ready fighter, and that it might then be purchased in substantial quantity.

That is what happened. There was a competitive fly-off between the two, which gave the nod to the General Dynamics' entry. Soon after, the USAF announced plans to purchase up to 650 of the little fighters. They would become part of the hi-lo mix, the compound word referring not to mission profiles, but to cost. Future USAF fighter fleets would be mixed, with a small number of versatile, expensive fighters and a larger number of less versatile, less-expensive fighters.

Current cost estimates for the YF-16 as developed into a production fighter vary between $4 and $5 million, with the majority view clustering around the lower end of

that range. Undoubtedly, escalation, inflation and the other enemies of constant cost will lay heavy influence on the development programme. Further, every fighter that has started out in pristine form has soon had all kinds of external and internal modifications added. Still further, the production cost of a large number of McDonnell-Douglas F-15 Eagles has been estimated as not too far above the $5 million mark, throwing another factor into the YF-16 equation.

But it is natural to expect that the YF-16 and YF-17 will be developed, and that they inexorably will grow heavier and more expensive. But at the same time, the same process will be happening to the F-15, and at some future point it may be possible to see an F-15 costing $20 million and an F-16 costing $8 million. And then, the Air Force will announce a competition for a revolutionary new concept in aircraft development: a fighter-type aircraft to use the very latest technology to achieve optimum performance at minimum cost.

There is no way of knowing certainly what the future will bring in technology,

General Dynamics YF-16
Crew: 1 *Powerplant:* 1 Pratt & Whitney
F100-P-100 afterburning turbofan engines,
23,400 lb thrust *Span:* 30 ft *Length:* 46·5 ft
Armament: 1 × 20-mm Vulcan cannon;
2 Sidewinder missiles *Speed:* Supersonic

but it may be instructive to look at the YF-16 and YF-17 to see what the present offers.

General Dynamics wanted to build the smallest and lightest aeroplane possible, using low-risk developments. They emphasised the air-superiority mission almost to the exclusion of any other possibility, and wound up with a single-place, single-engine airplane built primarily of conventional materials.

Northrop, with the experience of a long line of small, light combat aircraft to draw upon, carried that series one step further forward in applying what they had learned in extrapolation of the technology. But they stressed the concept of an operational prototype, one that could make the transition from development to production and service with a minimum of change and difficulty.

The YF-16 is a blended wing-body configuration, in which the contours of wing and fuselage are aerodynamically melded to a smooth and continuous fairing of surfaces. This was done to draw on body lift; the resulting wing size is smaller, and therefore lighter, and therefore cheaper. The wing has leading-edge manoeuvring flaps, which are programmed to function automatically as Mach number and angle of attack change in flight. They increase the camber of the wing and the lift at altitude.

Strakes – long, thin, horizontal fences ahead of the wing leading edge – are placed there to generate vortices. These rotating streams of energised air then move aft, and keep the boundary-layer flow from breaking away in the intersection area between

The YF-17, Northrop's latest idea for a low-cost lightweight fighter, has similar performance and armament to the YF-16, and in spite of its twin-jet configuration the two designs are strikingly similar

wing and fuselage. All these features – the blended wing-body shape, the leading-edge manoeuvring flaps, the strakes – work to improve the lift characteristics of the aircraft, especially at high altitudes and high angles of attack that are typical of dog-fighting. And they save weight also – General Dynamics say that the wing-body blending saved them about 320 lb in the fuselage, and another 250 on the wing. The strakes made a smaller wing possible, saving another 490 lb.

Weight saved means money saved. A pound of aircraft weight represents many dollars in direct labour and material costs, plus indirect research, development, design, engineering, and tooling costs. In aircraft, smaller means lighter means cheaper.

In order to get a very agile fighter, General Dynamics engineers deliberately reduced static stability, because a stable aircraft – while desirable for cruise flight and other portions of a mission – is not the best for manoeuvring. Next, they designed

55

British Aircraft Corporation

British Aircraft Corporation

An interceptor version of the MRCA (Multi-Role Combat Aircraft) is scheduled to replace RAF Phantoms and Lightnings in the air-superiority role for the 1980s. Different versions of the MRCA will be equipped with extremely advanced avionics for a wide range of different combat roles

in a fly-by-wire system, making the YF-16 the first aircraft planned from the start around such a control system. Fly-by-wire uses electronics to transfer the input signal from the pilot's control stick to the moveable surface; it reduces weight and vulnerability of the airplane. But it does more; it can be used to give unusual groupings of control motions, something no conventionally rigged system could do. In a combat situation, a pilot could easily pop up his airplane above the enemy on his tail by using fly-by-wire signals to move all of the horizontal surfaces to generate lift simultaneously. On an enemy's tail, he could aim the fuselage independently of what flight path his plane was following.

Further recognising that the pilot is under maximum physical stress during combat, the YF-16 design team slanted the pilot's seat back to a 30° angle, to increase his tolerance to high-g turns, and to make it easier for him to see and to look around in those situations. They gave him a side-arm controller instead of a central control stick.

By using a simple engine inlet under the belly, General Dynamics engineers saved another major weight increment. The inlet duct is short, and its leading edge is fixed, rather than built with the sharp-edged

variable geometry of most supersonic fighters. In the speed range where the YF-16 will fight, the complexity is unnecessary.

Finally, they built the airplane out of familiar aluminium alloys, with minimum use of steel and titanium. There is some use of graphite epoxy skins on the tails for stiffness with reduced weight, but that is the only area where new and different materials are used.

One novel feature of the overall design is that many of these features can be removed and replaced if they should not prove to be what they were predicted to be. The entire wing is quickly removeable, and can either be replaced, or moved back along the fuselage to restore some of the static stability designed out of the layout. The forward strakes can come off, the inlet can be simply changed, the canopy can be replaced, and even the side-arm controller can be removed and replaced by a central control stick in the conventional manner.

Northrop were faced with the same set of conditions, and it is interesting to note that their solutions differ in detail but not so much in concept. The twin-tailed YF-17

uses a pair of engines, rather than the single jet of the YF-16. Paired engines present unique problems, among which is 'base drag', that portion of the total airplane drag due to the blunt end of the jet exhaust. Northrop has been working on the problem a long time and the YF-17 is claimed to have the lowest base drag of any twin-jet fighter.

The wing is basically the wing of the Tiger II, with extra leading-edge extensions which reach well forward along the fuselage and which serve basically the same purpose as the YF-16's strakes: generation of strong vortex flow to re-energise the wing root boundary layer flow. But rather than relax the stability standards, Northrop chose to handle the vortex flow by using twin tails, canted outboard, and placed far forward on the fuselage. Here they also serve to close an aerodynamic gap between the wing trailing edge and the horizontal tail, and

MOD

they do not require a carry-through structure that pierces the rear fuselage. That means a lighter fuselage back there, and also an engine bay free of internal obstructions. The engines can be easily dropped out for maintenance or replacement.

The horizontal tail is larger than usual, and was sized for manoeuvring to give the best turning rate at high speeds. It is set as far back as possible, which means a slightly heavier and longer fuselage, but Northrop think that the manoeuvring advantages outweigh the objections in this case.

The YF-17 also uses fly-by-wire, but on the ailerons only. The control stick is the conventional central one, and the pilot's seat is tilted aft to an 18° angle. Like its competitor, the YF-17 is largely aluminium alloys with some graphite composite skins. One nice detail is the use of fireproofing paint in the engine bay. The paint expands under the heat and creates an air-filled insulating layer which effectively can contain and delay the fire for longer periods of time than usual.

These two aircraft characterise the best aerodynamic features and the best structural techniques available to designers today, given the restraints of the programme.

Heart of the fighter

Powerplants are the heart of the fighter. The technology of today's afterburning turbofans is a far cry from the inventions of von Ohain and Whittle. New metals, much higher temperatures, improved fuels and better internal flow characteristics have all added their incremental improvements to those early engines. The general feeling in the engine industry is that future changes are going to continue to be incremental, as better materials come along to permit higher operating temperatures. There should be no major changes in powerplant design for perhaps another decade.

Weaponry, another major factor in fighter design, is considered in the succeeding chapter.

The Israel Aircraft Industries Kfir, essentially a revamped Mirage III, was revealed in April 1975. Maximum speed is around Mach 2·2; armament is a 30-mm cannon plus missiles and stores of various types

Today, the over-riding considerations of costs are in the minds of every planner and designer of fighter aircraft. It can be expected that there will be at least one round of lightweight and low-cost fighters of the YF-16/YF-17 type. The success of translating those prototypes into operational fighters will determine to a large extent whether there will be a second round.

The future is not clear. It is difficult to see a follow-up as being more complex, more versatile and with higher performance than today's breeds. Besides, the fighter cannot be considered alone, but must be treated as part of an overall strategic battlefield system, working with ground troops and weaponry, airborne command and control systems, and perhaps in the context of long-range missile strikes as well as bomber and fighter-bomber assaults.

Consequently, the future trend of fighter design will be affected primarily by the overall defence programme of any country. It has been decided in the United States, for example, that there will be no more manned interceptors. The British once decided that there would be no more manned fighters at all after the Lightning.

It is possible that the current round of fighters could be the last. The average life of today's types is predicted to be about ten years at the beginning of their programme lives. Yet as the ten-year mark approaches, ways are found to stretch that life. Look at two fighters in large-scale service today. The Russian MiG-21 first flew in 1955; the McDonnell-Douglas F-4 prototype in 1958. Both are still very much the front-line fighters of their respective countries and allies, far from the end of their useful lives.

Applying that kind of a life span to the F-14 through F-17 series gets close to the end of this century. What will be the state of international affairs then? Will multilateral agreements have been worked out that will systematically reduce armaments? Or will an apocalypse of natural forces – lack of pure air and water, a starved earth and stagnant oceans – be controlling our international relations?

It's safer to look at the short-term approach. For the foreseeable future, the YF-16/YF-17 will be the route of future fighter development.

SEPECAT Jaguar S2
The first prototype of this tactical strike fighter flew in 1968. It will equip several RAF and *Armee de l'Air* squadrons
Crew: 2 *Powerplant:* 2 Rolls-Royce Turboméca RT172 Adour 102 turbofans, 4620 lb thrust each *Span:* 28·5 ft *Length:* 53·8 ft *Weight:* 23,000 lb *Apartment:* 1 × 30-mm cannon; 10,000 lb ordnance load *Speed:* Mach 1·6 at 33,000 ft

EJECTOR SEATS

John Batchelor

Martin-Baker Mk IV Ejector Seat
A fully automatic ejector seat incorporating a half second delay and a duplex drogue system. Ejection with this seat took place at the rate of 80 ft per second; it was the standard British ejector seat in the mid-1950s. The photo sequence above shows a pilot ejecting from a Meteor at ground zero

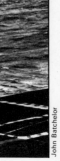

John Batchelor

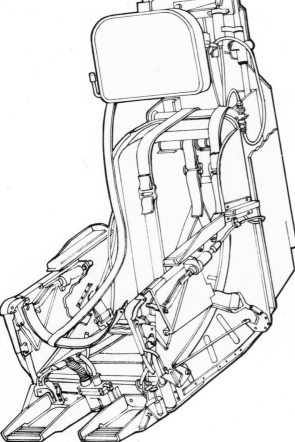

US Ejector Seat

This is the model of ejector seat fitted to the Sabre fighter; ejection was effected by means of a cartridge exploding under the seat to propel it into the air. The photo sequence below shows a Crusader making a bad landing on the deck of an aircraft carrier; as the plane goes overboard into the sea the pilot is shot to safety by his seat

Associated Press

FIGHTER ARMAMENT
CHOOSE YOUR WEAPON

The first jet fighters carried cannon, with some experimental air-to-air rockets on German planes. Since then, cannon, for weight of fire, and machine-guns, for maximum rpm, have vied for popularity, while missiles almost took over

Guns to missiles to guns and missiles is the short history of fighter armament.

At the end of the Second World War, most of the standard fighters on the Allied side were armed with machine-guns, characterised by a high rate of fire. Cannon had been introduced on the German fighters, and on some of the Allied types, and there was some use of unguided air-to-air rockets by the Germans.

This mixed weaponry set a trend that has continued to this day. Since then, fighters have been armed with machine-guns, cannon and unguided rockets, plus a newer development, the guided missile.

Most early jet fighters were armed with cannon. The value of the heavier weapon had been proved during the Second World War. Only in the United States was there a holdout position for the machine-gun, and not until the Korean war did the military finally make an all-out switch away from those weapons.

It would seem obvious that a cannon is better than a machine-gun; it fires a heavier shell, and therefore has greater striking power. It also has a generally higher muzzle velocity and greater range, both desirable attributes. But there is a strong argument for the 'buzz-saw' theory of aircraft armament. A cluster of six or eight heavy calibre machine-guns can bring an effective weight of fire upon an enemy aircraft that is sufficient to cut it to pieces – literally. There is a problem, though; the firing has to be done within effective range, and it must be accurately aimed.

Korean combat of jet against jet introduced a new element. That kind of combat stretched the combat range of the machine-gun to the point where it was no longer effective. The ranges were increased substantially from those the USAF pilots had grown used to in their previous war. And eight machine-guns at those distances were often totally ineffective. Strikes could be seen on the MiGs, but the Russian-built planes absorbed them and continued to fly and fight.

A Lockheed F-94C Starfire fires a salvo of rockets over the California Desert in 1952. Inset: 'Phantom' effect of heat condensation as a Lightning fires its three 30-mm cannon

Keystone

Actually, two things were happening: the range had opened up, and the airplanes had grown more rugged. The speed of jet aircraft dictated thicker skins, approaching the thickness of armour plating in some cases. And, hit at a shallow angle in the classic tail-chase, those surfaces were almost as good as armour in deflecting machine-gun bullets.

Korea, then, spelled the end of the machine-gun as an armament for jet fighters. As cannon batteries took their place, certain national characteristics began to emerge. The United States standardised on the 20-mm cannon; Europe built around the heavier 30-mm weapon. The Russians tried several – they have used 20-mm, 23-mm and 37-mm cannon in their fighters.

Conventional designs of aircraft cannon lacked the really high rate of fire that fighter pilots wanted. A fierce combat gives very little time to a pilot to aim and fire. He wants to be able to fire a maximum weight of slugs in minimum time.

There are two apparent ways to solve this problem, and the United States and Europe took different paths. The European developments generally were based on the revolving chamber concepts that were evolved by Mauser in Germany during the Second World War. The United States reached back into history to the Gatling gun, a 19th Century field weapon with a multiple barrel. The six barrels rotated and fired as they came opposite the breech mechanism. The Gatling patents were a basis for the modern 20-mm Vulcan cannon with an awesome rate of fire which reaches 6000 rpm.

But while these developments were going on, significant changes were being made in overall fighter armament concepts. For one thing, the guided and unguided rockets were beginning to come into their own. By the mid-1950s, just a few short years after the start of the Korean war, the first air-to-air guided missiles began to appear. Early guidance methods were improved, and homing missiles evolved, able to fly unerringly towards an enemy by reading his radar reflection, or his infrared signature, and homing on it.

It was only a matter of time until the nuclear weapons that had once filled bomb bays were reduced in size to fit into the warheads of air-to-air missiles. Unguided, because their lethal radius was so great that guidance would have been gilding the lily, these weapons were carried as standard armament on USAF interceptors for many years. They since have been replaced by a further updating, a smaller nuclear device in a guided weapon.

In fighter-against-bomber combat, the fighter held the speed advantage for many years. The standard way to shoot down a bomber was to approach from the rear in a tail chase, or a curve of pursuit as it was more elegantly called. The fighter pilot kept the nose of his aircraft bearing on the enemy target, and when he was within range of the bomber, the bomber was within range of him, and he was often met with a blast of fire from the enemy.

Obviously the curve of pursuit had drawbacks as a fighter tactic. But to replace it with anything else would seem to call for superhuman skill in piloting, because from any other approach angle, the speed differentials in the approach and the rapidly changing bearing of the target made hitting it more a matter of luck than skill.

The Germans developed a different tactical manoeuvre: they flew their jet interceptors in a line abeam at right angles to the bomber stream, and fired salvos of unguided rockets into the stream. They had to be successful; the densities of the bomber stream and the rocket salvos were so high that missing was impossible.

This technique was refined for single interceptors after the war. Armed with unguided rockets, the interceptor would fly against its target on an intersecting path, called a lead-collision course, heading for the point in the sky where the bomber would be when the interceptor's missiles got there. This called for skill in piloting and firing, and it was inevitable that a simple computing sight would be developed for this particularly difficult situation.

But the unguided rocket was short-lived, and was soon replaced by a guided missile with a brain of its own. It could change course to match any last-second evasion by the bomber, and it was infinitely more accurate than the unguided rockets.

In a sense, then, armament for the fighter-against-bomber combat evolved from an airplane carrying guns to a two-stage missile. The first stage, of course, is the

Associated Press

A US Navy F-14 Tomcat with its load of Phoenix missiles. In 1973 a world record was set when a Phoenix scored a hit on a supersonic jet drone at 126 miles range. They were introduced into service in 1973/74

Republic F-105D Thunderjet
This long-range fighter-bomber typifies the weight of armament carried by modern combat planes
 Crew: 1 *Powerplant:* 1 Pratt & Whitney J75-P-19W, 17,200 lb thrust *Span:* 35 ft
Length: 64·2 ft *Weight:* 38,034 lb
Armament: 1×20-mm cannon; 8000 lb internal plus 6000 lb external ordnance load
Speed: Mach 2·1 at 36,000 ft

Supermarine Scimitar
This naval fighter was a victim of the swing towards missiles in the late 1950s, when its original armament of four 30-mm cannon was replaced by four Sidewinder missiles
 Crew: 1 *Powerplant:* 2 Rolls-Royce Avon 202, 11,250 lb thrust each *Span:* 37·1 ft
Length: 55·3 ft *Weight:* 27,000 lb
Armament: 4×30-mm cannon
Speed: 710 mph at 10,000 ft

00484

carrying airplane; the second stage is the guided weapon which delivers the warhead.

Fighter-fighter combat was and remains different. No matter how carefully planned are the tactics, and no matter if the first salvos are made on a lead-collision intercept basis, the contact soon swings into a swirling dog-fight, with the simple objective of getting on the enemy's tail. In the Korean war and subsequently, typical fighting ranges were on the order of 500 to 750 yards; beyond those ranges, the chances of kills were greatly reduced.

With guided missiles, that range could be increased greatly; ranges of several thousand yards were thought of as typical for the missiles. And so, fighter designs switched to an armament of all missiles, and the cannon was considered obsolete. Air-to-air missiles, either with radar or infrared homing, were further developed and became the standard weapons to the exclusion of anything else.

And then there was another war, in Southeast Asia, and there it became obvious that a gun was an absolute necessity for air-to-air combat. Missiles did not do so well at short ranges. And there were times when the enemy fighters did not stay off at long ranges, as they so often had in Korea – this time, the enemy fighters were eager to

Most modern jet fighters have some strike capability: here a Phantom drops napalm over Vietnam

close for combat. In such situations a fighter pilot calls for guns – and fast. The answer was supplied in the form of external podded guns that could be hung below the wings of fighters for either air-to-air combat or strafing ground positions.

Those external stores, of course, slow the fighter, and may even reduce its manoeuvrability considerably, so they were not the ideal solution. Further, the guns were distant from the pilot, robbing him of that aiming feeling that he normally has with guns on the fuselage centreline. Finally, unless the pods were unusually rigid, and rigidly mounted, they might deflect enough under the loads of firing to increase the scatter and degrade the accuracy of the burst. At best the pods were a temporary solution for fighter-fighter combat.

As one result of the Vietnam action, guns have been reintroduced into USAF fighters where they had been lacking. (The Navy had never given them up.) Nor did most designers succumb to the siren call of the missiles. Very few European and Russian fighters have been built during the last 30 years around a missile battery only.

As the weapons progressed from form to form, so did the rest of the armament system. Gunsights, which were simple optical types with a lead-angle computer in early jet fighters, soon added more and more semi-automatic features. Today, firing controls range from the nearly automatic to the automatic. In a modern interceptor, it is possible for the pilot to find, fix and destroy his target without ever seeing it, or initiat-

ing any action except arming the system and the weapons. The automatic systems on board have searched for the target, found it, locked on to it, computed its position, corrected the aircraft course, moved into firing position, released the weapon, and confirmed the destruction of the enemy target, and all without the touch of the pilot's hands.

For interception missions, this is the future, as well as the present, until the unmanned guided missiles take over completely. For air-to-air combat between fighters, the trend is back to the automatic cannon with a high rate of fire, like the Vulcan. For fighter against bomber, the future is the same as that of the interceptor.

For the common foray against ground targets, there are whole packages of weapons that can be loaded under the wings.

Future fighters will continue to be armed as in the past. They will carry a single cannon battery with a high rate of fire, and probably a pair of long-range dog-fight

missiles. They will have strong points under the wing and fuselage for a variety of external weapons. The fire-control systems will be advanced and semi-automatic, with an automatic mode for intercept or all-weather missions. Sighting data will be shown on the windshield in a head-up display.

General Dynamics YF-16 fighters taking off

Flight International

This series of special publications presents full accounts of various aspects of war and warfare. Written by experts and superbly illustrated by John Batchelor, they describe developments in design and armament, combat techniques and military applications during two World Wars. Copies should still be available through your newsstand, but in case of difficulty write direct to History of the Second World War, 6 Commercial St., Hicksville, N.Y. 11801, enclosing check or money order, payable to History of the Second World War, for $2.00 per Special to include postage costs.